Popping With Power
Book C — Grades 3-4

EDITORS

Arthur Wiebe
Project Director
Fresno Pacific College

Larry Ecklund
Project Director
Fresno Pacific College

Judith Hillen
Assoc. Project Director
Fresno Pacific College

PROJECT FACILITATOR

Jeri Starkweather
Fresno Pacific College

WRITING TEAM

Sean Greene
Third-Fourth Grade Teacher
Madera Unified School District
Madera, California

Helen Crossley
Elementary School Principal
Rialto Unified School District
Rialto, California

Susan Dixon
Math Teacher
Rialto Unified School District
Rialto, California

Loretta Hill
GATE Teacher
Fair Oaks School
Oakdale, California

Helen Rayfield
Fourth Grade Teacher
Mendota Union School District
Mendota, California

Anne Rudig
Sixth Grade Teacher
Visalia Unified School District
Visalia, California

Carol Bland
Third Grade Teacher
Westside Elementary School District
Five Points, California

Gina Wiens
Fourth Grade Teacher
Central Union School District
Stratford, California

Nancy Williams
Fifth Grade Teacher
Delhi School District
Delhi, California

ILLUSTRATOR

Kathleen House

i

AIMS (Activities Integrating Mathematics and Science) began in 1981 with a grant from the National Science Foundation. The non-profit AIMS Education Foundation publishes hands-on instructional materials (books and the monthly AIMS Newsletter) that integrate curricular disciplines such as mathematics, science, language arts, and social studies. The Foundation sponsors a national program of professional development through which educators may gain both an understanding of the AIMS philosophy and expertise in teaching by integrated, hands-on methods.

Table of Contents

Index of Skills

MATH SKILLS

SCIENCE PROCESSES

I HEAR, AND I FORGET
I SEE, AND I REMEMBER
I DO, AND I UNDERSTAND

-Chinese Proverb

Introduction

Popping With Power is a book exploding with hands-on investigations integrating math skills and science relationships in our physical world. In this book, students become machinists, engineers, and electricians as they investigate questions such as: How do machines make life easier? Can time be kept with a pendulum? How long can you keep an ice cube from melting? How does color affect temperature? Which materials carry the strongest electrical charge? How does the force of wind affect a suspension bridge? How could you throw a heavy ball over a wall?

For solutions to these probing mysteries, students will energetically operate machines to simplify work, swing and time pendulums and bouncing balls, creatively insulate ice cubes, and observe color affects on temperature. Their interest will be charged as they determine which materials carry the strongest electrical charge, how the forces of wind are an enemy to bridges, and how to catapult heavy boulders.

Electrify your students' natural curiosity and enthusiasm about energy and their world with the boundless activities presented in Popping With Power.

TAKE IT EASY

I. Topic Area
Simple Machines

II. Introductory Statement
Students will learn how the six simple machines work.

III. Math Skills
a. Counting

Science Processes
a. Observing and classifying
b. Gathering and recording data
c. Interpreting data

IV. Materials
1 class set of the 6 simple machines
"Suggestions"

inclined plane
slide
various ramps

pulley
drapes
flagpoles

wedge
knives
forks
sewing needles

wheel and axle
doorknobs
toy cars
fishing pole

lever
hammer
bottle opener

gear wheels
hand drill
hand mixer
bicycle

1 class set of task cards
"Examples"

inclined plane
1. Roll the toy car down the ramp.

wedge (sewing needle)
1. Stick the needle into the cloth.
2. Pull the needle out.

lever (hammer)
1. Hammer the nail into the block of wood.
2. Use the hammer to pull the nail out.

pulley (drapes)
1. Use the cords to close the drapes.
2. Now open the drapes.

wheel and axle (doorknob)
1. Open the door using the knob.
2. Close the door with the knob.

gear wheels (hand drill)
1. Turn the handle of the drill so the point goes into the block of wood.
2. Pull the drill out of the wood.

materials to perform each task
chart paper

V. Key Question
Why do machines make your life easier?

VI. Background Information
There are six simple machines.
1. Inclined plane: A slanted surface, which is sometimes called a ramp.

2. Wedge: Two inclined planes joined together to form a sharp edge.
3. Lever: A bar resting on a turning point (fulcrum).
4. Pulley: A wheel with a rope moving around it.
5. Wheel and axle: A wheel that turns on a rod.
6. Gear wheel: A wheel with teeth.

VII. Management
1. A class period of 50-60 minutes.
2. Class divided into six working groups.
3. Set up a station for each machine.
4. Groups will rotate through the stations.

VIII. Procedure
1. Gather the six simple machines.
2. Prepare a task card for each machine.
3. Set up the six stations.
4. Prepare a chart size copy of the student worksheet.

IX. What the Students Will Do
Do the following at each station:
1. Record the name of the object.
2. Perform the job on the task card.
3. Record the job each object does.

Total Class
4. Record data from each group on class chart.

X. Discussion
1. Discuss how and why each simple machine works. (During discussion students will fill in information on student worksheet.)
2. How many simple machines do you see around the classroom (desk, playground, etc.)?
3. What are some of the machines you found?
4. Which kind of simple machine did you find the most of?
5. Which kind of simple machine was hardest to find?
6. How did we discover that simple machines make tasks in life easier?

XI. Extensions
1. Discover what parts of your body are simple machines.
2. Show "Donald Duck in Math Magic Land" (film—part IV)
3. Check your home for simple machines.

XII. Curriculum Coordinates
1. Write a poem about three simple machines.
2. Write a paragraph comparing and contrasting two simple machines.
3. Draw a picture of some simple machines in your own bedroom.
4. Do some physical exercise using the various portions of your body that are simple machines.

NAME _____

TAKE IT EASY

1. GO TO EACH STATION.
2. OBSERVE THE MACHINE - READ THE TASK CARD - DO THE JOB.
3. RECORD THE OBJECT AND JOB AT EACH STATION ON THIS WORKSHEET.
4. CLASS DISCUSSION WILL FOLLOW.

STATION	OBJECT	JOB	HOW IT WORKS	NAME OF MACHINE
1				
2				
3				
4				
5				
6				

z-z-z

NAME _____

TAKE IT EASY

MACHINE	QUANTITY	EXAMPLES	
INCLINED PLANE		A. _____ D. _____ B. _____ E. _____ C. _____ F. _____	
WEDGE		A. _____ D. _____ B. _____ E. _____ C. _____ F. _____	
LEVER		A. _____ D. _____ B. _____ E. _____ C. _____ F. _____	
PULLEY		A. _____ D. _____ B. _____ E. _____ C. _____ F. _____	
WHEEL AND AXLE		A. _____ D. _____ B. _____ E. _____ C. _____ F. _____	
GEAR WHEELS		A. _____ D. _____ B. _____ E. _____ C. _____ F. _____	

3

WORKING TOGETHER

I. Topic Area
Compound Machines

II. Introductory Statement
Students will learn about compound machines.

III. Math Skills
a. Counting
b. Graphing

Science Processes
a. Gathering and recording data
b. Interpreting data
c. Observing and classifying

IV. Materials
chart paper
samples of compound machines
"Suggestions"
   bicycle
   hand drill
   scissors

V. Key Question
How many compound machines did you see on your way to school today?

VI. Background Information
1. The knowledge of simple machines would be prerequisite learning.
2. A compound machine is made up of two or more simple machines to do a job.
   Examples:
   Bicycle—wheel and axle, inclined plane, gear wheels
   Hand drill—wheel and axle, wedge shapes
   Scissors—wedges; two levers joined at a fulcrum

VII. Management
1. A class period of 50-60 minutes with an optional 30 minute independent follow-up.
2. Divide the students into small groups with a leader.
3. The leader should be responsible and will have to study the information ahead of time.
4. Groups will visit different areas at school looking for compound machines (playground, office, kitchen, classroom).

VIII. Procedure
1. Prepare charts.
2. Arrange tour of school kitchen and office.
3. Get some examples of compound machines.

IX. What the Students Will Do
1. Review the six simple machines and how they work.
2. Look at examples of compound machines.
3. Tour the office, classroom, kitchen, and playground. Look for examples of compound machines.
4. Record your findings on the student worksheet.
5. Transfer your findings to a bar graph.

X. Discussion
1. What compound machines did you find?
2. What simple machines were in each of the compound machines you found?
3. In which area of the school were the most compound machines found?
4. Why do you think this is so?
5. Can you think of ten different compound machines you'd find in your home?

XI. Extensions
1. Take a more complicated machine (radio, engine) and try to identify the simple machines involved.
2. Actually build your compound machine invention for a class demonstration.
3. As a class construct a compound machine to help the students do some simple task more efficiently.
4. Try to create your own compound machine to do an inventive task. Examples: shoelace tier, face-washing machine, bubble gum blower, garbage taker outer, exercising machine for fish.
5. Label your own invention with the simple machines that make it up.

XII. Curriculum Coordinates
1. Write a story about your compound machine invention.
2. While at P.E. try to identify the machines you are playing on.
3. Construct a toothpick model of your compound machine invention.

WORKING TOGETHER

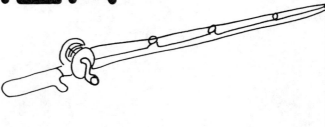

COMPOUND MACHINES I FOUND:

CLASSROOM	OFFICE	PLAYGROUND	KITCHEN

POPPING WITH POWER

NAME _____

WORKING TOGETHER MACHINE

NO.	CLASSROOM	OFFICE	PLAYGROUND	KITCHEN
14				
13				
12				
11				
10				
9				
8				
7				
6				
5				
4				
3				
2				
1				

POPPING WITH POWER

MAGNETS ARE ATTRACTIVE

I. **Topic Area**
   Magnets

II. **Introductory Statement**
   Students will learn to recognize objects that will be attracted to magnets and the magnet's attraction power.

III. **Key Question**
   What are some different uses for a magnet?

IV. **Math Skills**
   a. Measurement
   b. Graphing
   c. Averaging
   d. Estimating

   Science Processes
   a. Observing and classifying
   c. Gathering and recording data
   d. Interpreting data

V. **Materials**
   magnets (enough for every 2-3 students)
   straight pins
   paperclips
   paper fasteners
   aluminum foil
   S.O.S. pad
   silver coins
   nails
   3 wood blocks of different thickness
   2 books—1 thick and 1 thin
   piece of paper
   paper folder
   centimeter rulers or tape measure

VI. **Management**
   1. This investigation will take 2 sessions. An introductory activity—30 minutes. The investigation will take approximately 45 minutes.
   2. A variety of shapes and sizes of magnets lends itself to further discussion, though horseshoe magnets should be avoided. The horseshoe magnets don't work well in some of the activities.
   3. Students should work in groups of 2 or 3.

VII. **Procedure**
   1. The teacher will set up the 4 stations.
      Station 1: Set out different objects, such as straight pins, paperclips, paper fasteners, aluminum foil, S.O.S. pad, silver coins, and nails.
      Station 2: Set out a box of paperclips.
      Station 3: Set out metric ruler or tape measure and a few paperclips.
      Station 4: Set out the wood blocks (label them 1, 2, 3, or A, B, C), 2 books (labeled 1 and 2 or A and B), a piece of paper, and a paper folder. Also needed at this station are a few paperclips and 2 or 3 metric rulers.

   2. At the end of the investigation, the teacher will graph each groups' average number of paperclips held by their magnet at station 2. The teacher should do this on a chart at the front of the room or on an overhead projector so it may be observed by all of the students.

VIII. **What the Students Will Do**
   1. *Introductory Activity*—Before receiving their magnets, the students will select 6 objects from their desk. 3 that they predict will be attracted to their magnet, and 3 that will not be attracted to their magnet.
   2. Students will be given time to explore the classroom with their magnets. At the teacher's discretion they may also explore outside the classroom.
   3. *Station 1*—Students will write the name of each object, then test whether it is attracted to the magnet. They will then check the appropriate box on their worksheet—yes, it is attracted, or no, it is not attracted.
   4. *Station 2*—Students will estimate how many paperclips their magnet will hold from end to end. They will test this 5 times and record their results each time. After testing 5 times, they will find the average number of paperclips held. Result will be recorded.
   5. *Station 3*—The students will place 1 paperclip at the end of a metric ruler or tape measure (front tip of paperclip at 0). Students will estimate the distance between the magnet and the paperclip when it is attracted. To test this, they will start the magnet at 30 cm and slowly move it closer to the paperclip. When the paperclip is drawn to the magnet, record the measurement.
   6. *Station 4*—Students will write the name of each object and then measure and record their thickness. They will place a paperclip on top of the object, and with the magnet underneath try to move the paperclip. Record results.

IX. **Discusssion**
   1. What objects were not attracted to your magnet? Why?
   2. Was there anything you could do to make more paperclips hold on end to end at *Station 2*? (If they rub the paperclip on the magnet first, they will make a longer chain.) Why does that help? (The paperclip becomes magnetized.)
   3. Compare the different magnets.

X. **Curriculum Coordinates**
   Social Studies
   1. Unit on compasses and orienteering.
   Science
   1. Make your own electromagnet.

7

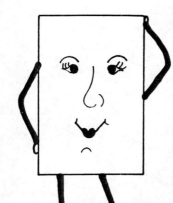

MAGNETS ARE ATTRACTIVE

PREDICTION: PICK 3 OBJECTS FROM YOUR DESK THAT WILL BE ATTRACTED TO YOUR MAGNET.

	YES	NO
1. _____	_____	_____
2. _____	_____	_____
3. _____	_____	_____

PREDICTION: PICK 3 OBJECTS FROM YOUR DESK THAT WILL NOT BE ATTRACTED TO YOUR MAGNET.

	YES	NO
1. _____	_____	_____
2. _____	_____	_____
3. _____	_____	_____

8

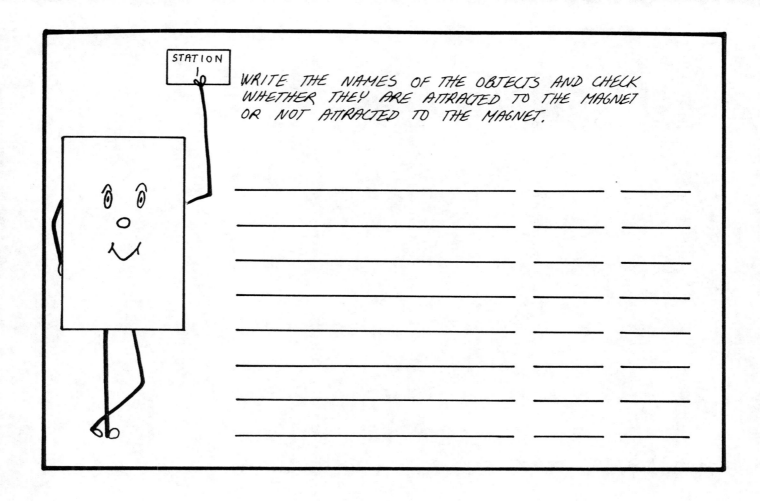

STATION 1

WRITE THE NAMES OF THE OBJECTS AND CHECK WHETHER THEY ARE ATTRACTED TO THE MAGNET OR NOT ATTRACTED TO THE MAGNET.

_____ _____ _____

_____ _____ _____

_____ _____ _____

_____ _____ _____

_____ _____ _____

_____ _____ _____

_____ _____ _____

_____ _____ _____

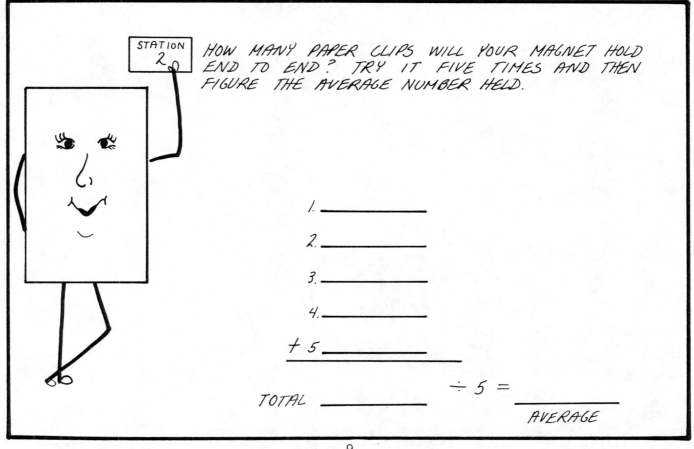

STATION 2

HOW MANY PAPER CLIPS WILL YOUR MAGNET HOLD END TO END? TRY IT FIVE TIMES AND THEN FIGURE THE AVERAGE NUMBER HELD.

1. _____

2. _____

3. _____

4. _____

+ 5 _____

TOTAL _____   ÷ 5 = _____

AVERAGE

9

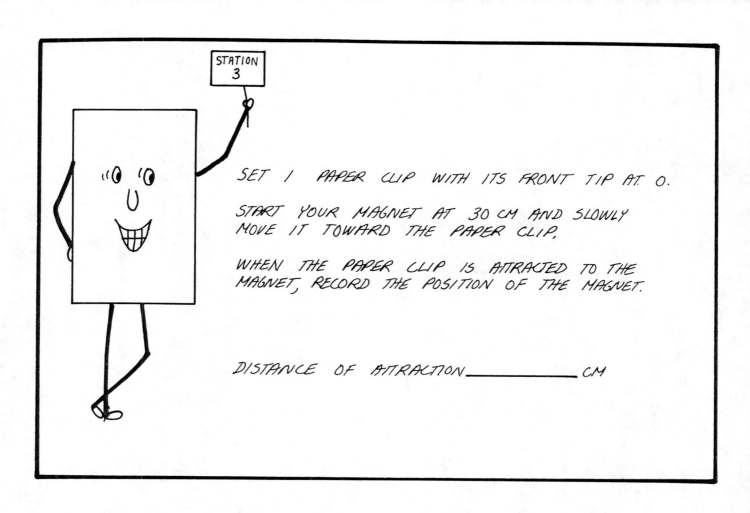

STATION 3

SET 1 PAPER CLIP WITH ITS FRONT TIP AT 0.

START YOUR MAGNET AT 30 CM AND SLOWLY MOVE IT TOWARD THE PAPER CLIP.

WHEN THE PAPER CLIP IS ATTRACTED TO THE MAGNET, RECORD THE POSITION OF THE MAGNET.

DISTANCE OF ATTRACTION_____ CM

STATION 4

MEASURE THE THICKNESS OF EACH OBJECT. RECORD. PLACE 1 PAPER CLIP ON TOP OF THE OBJECT AND THE MAGNET UNDERNEATH.

TEST WHETHER THE PAPER CLIP WILL MOVE THROUGH THE OBJECT. CHECK YES OR NO.

OBJECT	THICKNESS	YES	NO
1.			
2.			
3.			
4.			
5.			
6.			

10

SWING IN TIME

I. Topic Area
Pendulums

II. Introductory Statement
Students will understand, the longer the string of the pendulum, the fewer number of swings.

III. Math Skills
a. Measurement
b. Graphing

Science Processes
a. Gathering and recording data
b. Interpreting data
c. Applying and generalizing
d. Estimating

IV. Materials
string
fishing weights (1 oz. and 2 oz. for each child)
metric ruler or tape
marker pens

V. Key Question
Can a person keep accurate time with a pendulum?

VI. Background Information
1. The angle of release has no affect on the total number of swings.
2. Swings are counted in periods. A period is a complete cycle back and forth.

VII. Management
1. This investigation will take 2 50-minute class periods.
2. Label fishing weights No. 1-1 oz. weight and No. 2-2 oz. weight.
3. *Optional*—using results from weight No. 1, students can predict what results will be with pendulum swinging for 1 minute. Worksheet is included.

VIII. Procedure
1. Teacher will need to prepare pendulums in advance. Measure 110 cm of string and tie to weight No. 1. Repeat for weight No. 2.
2. Hold pendulum at designated interval and pull weight back at 45° angle. See diagram.

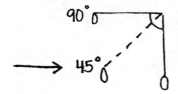

3. Teacher will time the swings for 30 seconds.

IX. What the Students Will Do
1. Students will measure and mark their string at 10 cm intervals (start measurement at the weight and mark up to 100 cm).
2. Students will begin by holding their pendulum at the 10 cm mark.
3. Students will count periods for 30 seconds and record results.
4. Repeat, holding string at 20 cm...50 cm.
5. Students should observe a pattern.
6. Students should be able to make a prediction for results at 60 cm...100 cm following the pattern.
7. Students should then record predictions and test.
8. *Day 2*—Repeat procedures No. 1-9 using weight No. 2.
9. Students will complete worksheets.

X. Discussion
1. How did different lengths of string affect the number of swings. (The longer the thread, the less number of swings.)
2. Did the heavier weight have any affect of the number of swings? (No)
3. Did you notice a number pattern as you recorded the number of swings?

XI. Extensions
1. Sand Pendulums—Make a cone-shaped cup and fill it with sand or salt. Let the sand or salt pour out from a hole in the bottom of the cone as it is swinging. Observe the pattern it makes.
2. Two or more pendulums at one time—Swing them in the same direction, opposite directions, 2 one way and 1 another, criss-cross...
3. Predict the amount of time it will take the pendulum to come to a complete stop.
4. Students should try to find a string length that will make the pendulum swing 60 times per minute.

NAME:_____

SWING IN TIME

WHAT DO YOU THINK THE RESULTS WOULD BE IF WE LET THE
PENDULUM SWING FOR _1 MINUTE?_

FILL OUT THE CHART FIRST, THEN WE'LL TRY IT WITH
WEIGHT #1.

YOUR ESTIMATE

10	20	30	40	50	60	70	80	90	100

10	20	30	40	50	60	70	80	90	100

ACTUAL NUMBER OF SWINGS

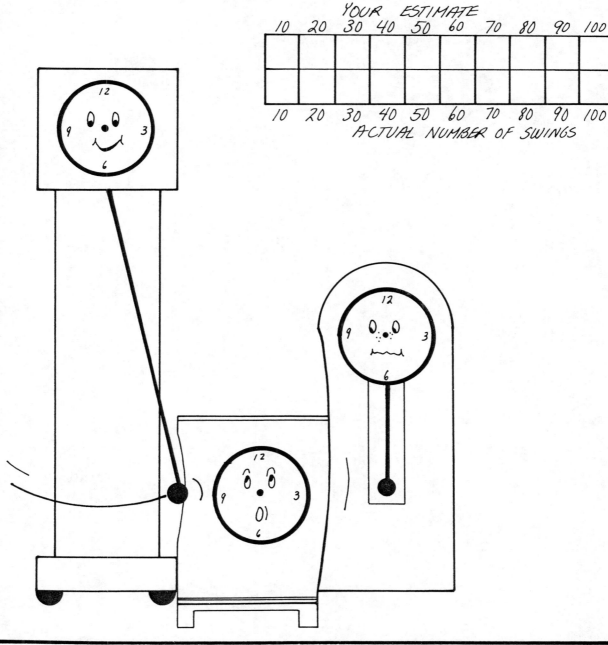

POPPING WITH POWER

NAME_____

SWING IN TIME

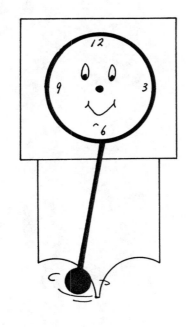

	10	20	30	40	50	60	70	80	90	100
ACTUAL #1										
YOUR ESTIMATE										

	10	20	30	40	50	60	70	80	90	100
ACTUAL #2										
YOUR ESTIMATE										

1. WHAT WAS THE MOST NUMBER OF SWINGS IN 30 SECONDS?

    #1 _____ #2 _____

2. WHAT WAS THE LEAST NUMBER OF SWINGS IN 30 SECONDS?

    #1 _____ #2 _____

3. WHAT WAS THE DIFFERENCE BETWEEN THE <u>MOST</u> NUMBER OF SWINGS FOR #1 AND #2?

4. WHAT WAS THE DIFFERENCE BETWEEN THE <u>LEAST</u> NUMBER OF SWINGS FOR #1 AND #2?

5. DID THE LENGTH OF THE STRING HAVE AN AFFECT ON THE NUMBER OF SWINGS? _____

6. DID THE WEIGHT HAVE AN EFFECT ON THE NUMBER OF SWINGS?

_____

©1987 AIMS Education Foundation

NAME _____

SWING IN TIME

WEIGHT
#1 GREEN

WEIGHT
#2 GREEN

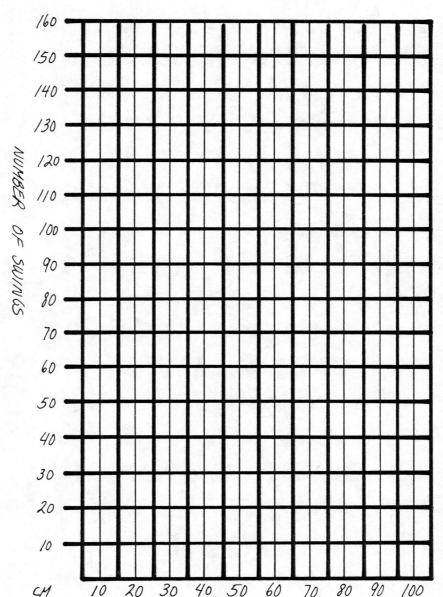

NUMBER OF SWINGS

160
150
140
130
120
110
100
90
80
70
60
50
40
30
20
10

CM   10 20 30 40 50 60 70 80 90 100

HAVE A BALL

I. Topic Area
Energy

II. Introductory Statement
Students will discover why some balls bounce higher than others.

III. Math Skills
a. Estimating
b. Measuring

Science Processes
a. Controlling variables
b. Predicting
c. Gathering and recording data
d. Observing and classifying
e. Applying and generalizing data

IV. Materials
5 balls of different size and weight
meter tape (included)
balance scale and centicubes
string

V. Key Question
"How high does a ball bounce?"

VI. Background Information
This investigation will help to introduce variables.

VII. Management
1. This investigation may take 45-50 minutes.
2. When measuring circumference, it may be helpful to wrap a length of string around the ball and then measure the length of string.
3. When measuring mass, any elementary balance scale and weights (centicubes) may be used.
4. Teacher should drop the balls.
5. It is important to have one observer to measure the height of the bounce and one to record the measurement.
6. Students may need practice in observing the height of the bounce.
7. Monitor student work.
8. Attach two-meter tape measure to wall (tape measure included).
9. Remember that the heighth of the bounce is the distance from the floor to the bottom of the ball at the height of the bounce (see diagram).

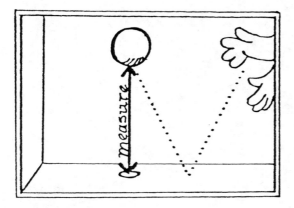

VIII. Procedure
1. Briefly talk about the similarities or differences of the balls.
2. Guide students in estimating, measuring and recording facts about the balls as described on the worksheet.
3. Select an observer and a recorder.
4. Drop the first ball from 150 cm. (you may need to repeat this step to get an accurate measurement.)
5. Repeat procedure until all balls have been bounced.
6. Record measurements on worksheet.

IX. What the Students Will Do
1. Write the names of the balls in the appropriate boxes.
2. Measure and record circumference of balls.
3. Measure and record mass of balls.
4. Estimate and record how high each ball will bounce.
5. Record actual height of bounce.
6. Write a description of each ball.

X. Discussion
1. Does the mass of the ball change the bounce?
2. Does the circumference of the ball change the bounce?
3. Did any results surprise you? Why?
4. Discuss variables (e.g., what would happen if you threw the balls down?)

XI. Extensions
1. Try dropping the balls from different heights.
2. Try dropping the balls on different surfaces.

XII. Curriculum Coordinates
Language Arts
1. Vocabulary extension.
Writing
1. Write a story about balls.
Art
1. Draw or paint your favorite activity with a ball.
Physical Education
1. Play any "ball" game (e.g., softball, kickball or basketball).

HAVE A BALL

1. ESTIMATE AND RECORD HOW HIGH EACH BALL WILL BOUNCE.

2. MEASURE AND RECORD THE ACTUAL HEIGHT OF THE BOUNCE OF EACH BALL.

3. MEASURE AND RECORD THE CIRCUMFERENCE OF EACH BALL.

4. MEASURE AND RECORD THE MASS OF EACH BALL.

5. RECORD A DESCRIPTION OF EACH BALL.

TYPE OF BALL	ESTIMATE HEIGHT OF BOUNCE	ACTUAL HEIGHT OF BOUNCE	MEASURE CIRCUMFERENCE	MEASURE MASS	DESCRIBE BALL

WRITE A SENTENCE THAT TELLS ABOUT THE CIRCUMFERENCE OF THE BALL AND THE BOUNCE OF THE BALL.

WRITE A SENTENCE THAT TELLS ABOUT THE MASS OF THE BALL AND THE BOUNCE OF THE BALL.

POPPING WITH POWER

HAVE ANOTHER BALL

I. **Topic Area**
   Energy

II. **Introductory Statement**
   Students will learn about the mechanics of bouncing.

III. **Math Skills**
   a. Whole number computation: subtraction
   b. Graphing
   c. Estimating
   d. Measurement in metric units

   Science Processes
   a. Controlling variables
   b. Predicting
   c. Gathering and recording data
   d. Observing and classifying
   e. Applying and generalizing

IV. **Materials**
   Golf balls for each student (or another firm ball).

V. **Key Question**
   How high does a ball bounce?

VI. **Background Information**
   1. This is a follow-up to "Have A Ball."
   2. If you have not talked about variables before, it would be helpful to briefly discuss variables.

VII. **Management**
   1. This investigation will take 20-30 minutes.
   2. Pair-up students to insure accurate measurements. (One to record and one to observe.)
   3. Students will need to release the ball the same way each time.
   4. Balls should not be thrown down. (Just dropped!)
   5. Monitor students work.
   6. Remember that the heighth of the bounce is the distance from the floor to the bottom of the ball at the height of the bounce.
   7. Students need to use the same surface to release the balls.

VIII. **Procedure**
   1. Pair-up students.
   2. Demonstrate how to release the ball.

IX. **What the Students Will Do**
   1. Estimate and record how high each ball will bounce.
   2. Record the actual height of bounce.
   3. Find the difference between the estimate and the actual bounce.
   4. Discuss how you can predict the height of the bounce using the data from the graph.

X. **Discussion**
   1. Was there a consistent pattern for the height of the bounce?
   2. What would happen if some students bounced the ball on different surfaces?
   3. What would happen if we used a different ball?

XI. **Extensions**
   1. Try using a different ball.
   2. Try a different surface.
   3. Try different heights.
   4. Make a chart to show the highest and lowest bounces.

XII. **Curriculum Coordinates**
   Language Arts
   1. Write about "Why Do Balls Bounce?"
   Physical Education
   1. Play soccer, basketball or your favorite "ball" game.
   Social Studies
   1. Learn about how balls are used in sports and how the balls have developed over the years.

HAVE ANOTHER BALL

1. ESTIMATE HOW HIGH THE BALL WILL BOUNCE AT EACH HEIGHT.

2. RELEASE THE BALL FROM EACH HEIGHT.

3. RECORD EACH HEIGHT OF BOUNCE.

4. SUBTRACT TO FIND THE DIFFERENCE BETWEEN THE ESTIMATE AND THE ACTUAL BOUNCE.

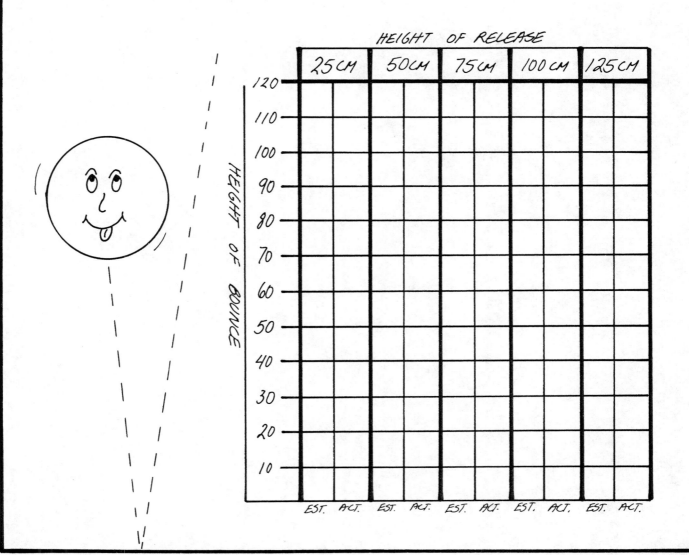

HEIGHT OF RELEASE

	25 CM		50 CM		75 CM		100 CM		125 CM	
EST.	ACT.	EST.	ACT.	EST.	ACT.	EST.	ACT.	EST.	ACT.	

HEIGHT OF BOUNCE: 120, 110, 100, 90, 80, 70, 60, 50, 40, 30, 20, 10

Roller Ball

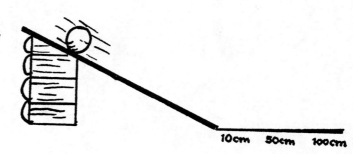

10cm   50cm   100cm

I. Topic Area
Energy

II. Introductory Statement
Students will discover how slope affects the distance a ball will roll.

III. Math Skills
a. Measuring
b. Graphing
c. Estimating
d. Subtracting

Science Processes
a. Controlling variables
b. Predicting
c. Gathering and recording data
d. Observing and classifying
e. Applying and generalizing data

IV. Materials
2 meter sticks
Golf ball
Books or blocks

V. Key Question
How far does a ball roll downhill?

VI. Background Information
This investigation helps to control variables. It may be helpful to do this investigation after "Have A Ball" and "Have Another Ball." "Roller Ball" introduces potential and kinetic energy.

VII. Management
1. This investigation will take 45 minutes.
2. Stack books or blocks to desired height ahead of time.
3. Tape the meter sticks together leaving a space for the ball to roll down.
4. Pre-measuring works best! Lay a piece of butcher paper along the "runway" with premeasured lengths.
5. Remember to release and not to push the ball.
6. It is importannt to have an observer measure the length of the roll.
7. Monitor student work for accurate recordings.

VIII. Procedure
1. Ask the key question.
2. Talk about variables. (What is a variable?)
3. Talk about slope. (Relate cars going uphill and downhill)
4. Discuss estimating and measuring.
5. Select an observer, recorder, and ball launcher.

IX. What the Students Will Do
1. Estimate and record distance of roll.
2. Release (no pushing) the ball from 5 cm.
3. Observe the rolling ball.
4. Record actual length of roll.
5. Subtract to find a difference between the estimate and actual.
6. Repeat for each height.

X. Discussion
1. Does slope affect the length of roll? Why or why not?
2. Did the ball go faster or slower when the slope was increased? Why?
3. Does the surface affect the roll of the ball?
4. How far would the ball roll from a 20 cm slope? From a 50 cm slope?
5. What would happen if the length of the runway is increased?

XI. Extensions
1. Try using different balls.
2. Try other slopes.
3. Try different surfaces.

XII. Curriculum Coordinates
Language Arts
1. Vocabulary extension (slope, variable, and estimate).
Writing
1. Have children make up a game with balls.
Physical Education
1. Play soccer or another favorite ball game.

ROLLER BALL

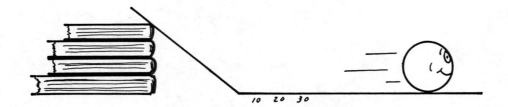

HOW FAR DOES A BALL ROLL DOWNHILL?

	ESTIMATE	ACTUAL	DIFFERENCE
5 CM			
10 CM			
15 CM			

1. ESTIMATE AND RECORD HOW FAR THE BALL WILL ROLL FROM 5 CM.

2. RECORD ACTUAL LENGTH OF ROLL.

3. SUBTRACT TO FIND A DIFFERENCE.

4. REPEAT FOR 10 CM AND 15 CM.

POPPING WITH POWER   ©1987 AIMS Education Foundation

BOUNCING BABY BALL

I. Topic Area
Energy

II. Introductory Statement
Students will discover how different surfaces affect the height of bounce.

III. Math Skills
a. Measuring
b. Estimating
c. Subtracting

Science Processes
a. Controlling variables
b. Predicting and hypothesizing
c. Gathering and recording data
d. Observing and classifying
e. Applying and generalizing

IV. Materials
A golf ball
meter stick
different surfaces (wood floor, cement floor, grass or others)

V. Key Question
What could make a ball bounce higher?

VI. Background Information
1. This investigation controls specific variables.
2. This investigation is the fourth in a series of investigations ("Have A Ball," "Have Another Ball," and "Roller Ball.").
3. It would be helpful to have done "Have A Ball" before doing this investigation.

VII. Management
1. This investigation will take 45-60 minutes.
2. Select different surfaces in or out of the classroom.

VIII. Procedure
1. Discuss variables.
2. Discuss controlling variables.
3. Discuss the different surfaces.
4. Discuss estimating, measuring and recording.
5. Select an observer.
6. Drop the ball from 100 cm. (You may need to repeat this step to get an accurate measurement.)
7. Repeat procedure for each surface.

IX. What the Students Will Do
1. Talk about the different surfaces.
2. Write the names of surfaces on worksheet.
3. Estimate and record height on worksheet.
4. Record actual height of bounce.
5. Subtract to find a difference.

X. Discussion
1. Why does the ball bounce differently on different surfaces?
2. Did any surfaces produce the same results?
3. Did any result surprise you?
4. What other variables affect height of bounce?

XI. Extensions
1. Try using different balls.
2. Try different heights.
3. Try unique surfaces (sand, water and paper).

XII. Curriculum Coordinates
Writing
1. Have students write up their own investigations on balls.
Physical Education
1. Play your favorite ball game.

NAME _____

BOUNCING BABY BALL

WHAT COULD MAKE A BALL BOUNCE HIGHER?

SURFACE	ESTIMATE	ACTUAL	DIFFERENCE

1. WHY DOES THE BALL BOUNCE DIFFERENTLY ON DIFFERENT SURFACES?

2. DID ANY SURFACES PRODUCE THE SAME RESULTS?

3. DID ANY RESULTS SURPRISE YOU?

4. WHAT OTHER VARIABLES AFFECT HEIGHT OF BOUNCE?

POLAR BRRRS

I. Topic Area
Physical Science (Cold Conservation)

II. Introductory Statement
Students will learn about insulation and refrigeration.

III. Math Skills
a. Whole number computation
b. Measurement: Metric weight
c. Graphing

Science Processes
a. Gathering and recording data
b. Applying and generalizing

IV. Materials
1 standardized ice cube per child

V. Key Question
How long can you keep an ice cube from melting?

VI. Background Information
1. Cold is the absence of heat.
2. Refrigeration by means of natural ice has been used for thousands of years. Ice cellars were used in China as early as 1,000 B.C. The Greeks and Romans stored packed snow for cooling wine in cellars insulated with grass, earth, and manure.
3. In 1834, Jacob Perkins got a British patent for the production of cold by expansion of volatile liquids in a closed cycle.

VII. Management
1. Initial planning by students should take place several days before the investigation occurs.
2. Allow children who forget their materials to use available classroom supplies.
3. On the day of the investigation, allow 1-2 hours to elapse between the time the Polar Brrs are set up and the time measurements are taken.
4. The class should be divided into groups of 2-3 children.

VIII. Procedure
1. The teacher will provide one standardized ice cube in a plastic bag for each group.
2. Each group will put their ice cube in their "Polar Brrr."
3. Beginning weight should be recorded on student worksheet.
4. "Polar Brrrs" may be kept on student desks or placed altogether in one place in the room.
5. At the given time, students should record how much time has elapsed.
6. Drain the melted water from the plastic bags.
7. Weigh the ice cubes. Record ending weight. Find the difference.

IX. What the Students Will Do
1. Refer to Student Worksheet.

X. Discussion
1. What is refrigeration? (the cooling or freezing of food or perishables for storage)
2. What is insulation? (something that retards the passage of heat, electricity, or sound)
3. What did people use before modern refrigeration? (ice cellars, packed snow, running cold water such as rivers, ice boxes)
4. Why do we need refrigeration? (to keep food from spoiling so quickly)

XI. Extensions
1. Put ice cubes in different places to test melt rates (in the sun, in the shade, in the fridge, in a closet, etc.)

XII. Curriculum Coordinates
Language Arts
1. Write poems on ICE, COLD, SHIVER, WINTER, etc.
2. Make a cartoon strip or write a story about "A Day In The Life Of An Ice Cube."

Social Studies
1. Visit an ice factory.
2. Make ice cream with an old-fashioned crank machine.
3. Talk with some "old timers" about ice trunks and summer memories.
4. Do research on: Ice cream, refrigerated box cars on trains, sundaes, refrigerators, ice cream cones, igloos, ancient methods of refrigeration, etc.

Art
1. Build an igloo from sugar cubes.
2. Make a class mural about the history of refrigeration.

NAME _____

POLAR BRRRS

HOW LONG CAN YOU KEEP AN ICE CUBE FROM MELTING?

TEAM MEMBERS _____
_____

ICE CUBE # _____

RULES: 1. YOU MAY BRING IN ANYTHING YOU WANT EXCEPT ELECTRICAL APPLIANCES, A THERMOS, OR AN ICE CHEST.
2. IT MUST FIT ON THE TOP OF YOUR DESK.
3. THE ICE CUBE MUST NOT MELT ALL OVER THE PLACE.

LIST THE MATERIALS YOU HAVE USED

DRAW A PICTURE OF YOUR "POLAR BRRR" AND LABEL THE PARTS.

_____
_____
_____
_____
_____

RECORD THE INFORMATION FOR YOUR OWN ICE CUBE.

[____] BEGINNING WEIGHT

−[____] ENDING WEIGHT

[____] DIFFERENCE

NAME_____

RECORD HOW MUCH TIME HAS ELAPSED._____ HOURS

ENDING WEIGHT
OF ICE CUBE
IN GRAMS

1   2   3   4   5   6   7   8   9   10   11   12   13   14

"POLAR BRRR" NUMBER

1. WHICH "POLAR BRRR" WORKED BEST?_____

2. WHY DID IT WORK BEST?_____

3. WHY DID YOU THINK YOUR "POLAR BRRR" WOULD WORK?_____
   _____

4. IF YOU HAD A CHANCE TO BUILD ANOTHER "POLAR BRRR," HOW
   WOULD YOU DO IT DIFFERENTLY?

   _____

   _____

5. QUICK! REVERSE YOUR THINKING. WHAT IS THE QUICKEST WAY
   YOU CAN THINK OF TO MELT AN ICE CUBE? (FIRE IS NOT
   ALLOWED).

   _____

   _____

POPPING WITH POWER   ©1987 AIMS Education Foundation

CARTONS 'N COTTON

I. Topic Area
Insulation—Energy Conservation

II. Introductory Statement
Students will discover the effectiveness of insulation.

III. Math Skills
a. Measuring
b. Computing—Subtraction with regrouping

Science Processes
a. Gathering and recording data
b. Observing and classifying
c. Predicting and hypothesizing
d. Interpreting data

IV. Materials
(per group)
3 small jars with lids—all same size (large baby food jars work great)
3 half-gallon milk cartons
glue
cotton balls (about 250-300)
thermometer
hot tap water
worksheet

V. Key Question
How do we use a blanket or covering to keep things warm?

VI. Background Information
It is helpful for the teacher to know that the carton with the cotton on the inside will be noticeably warmer than the other 2 cartons.

VII. Management
1. Three class periods of 45 minutes each. It is better to make the insulated milk cartons one day and do the experiment the next. The math paper was completed the third day.
2. Groups of 4-6 are recommended. Size of groups should be determined by the number of thermometers and supplies available.
3. Before passing milk cartons out to the students, the teacher needs to cut a door large enough for easy access to the jars.
4. It is better to have three thermometers per group, but it can be done with just one.

VIII. Procedure
Day One
Assign groups. Pass out glue, cotton balls, and milk cartons. Students will glue cotton balls on the inside of one carton and on the outside of the second

carton. Be sure students include all sides, top, and bottom. The third carton will remain untouched.
Day Two
Collect all necessary materials. Give each student a worksheet. Go through "What the Students Will Do" step by step. As the students are waiting during the first 15 minute timing period have them sequence the steps gone through so far. The teacher can write these on the board for the students to copy. This gives the student a set of directions to use at home. Don't forget to include the gluing of cotton balls from the previous day. Record temperatures after the second 15 minute period. Discuss what is happening.
Day 3
Do computation on worksheet. Discuss results.

IX. What the Students Will Do
1. Students will insulate one carton by gluing cotton balls to the inside of the carton on all sides, top, and bottom.
2. Students will insulate one carton by gluing cotton balls to the outside of the carton on all sides, top, and bottom.
3. Students will leave the third carton untouched.
4. Fill all three jars with the same amount of hot tap water.
5. Put a thermometer in each jar and record temperature on worksheet. If group has only one thermometer work quickly but give the thermometer time to register in each jar.
6. Remove thermometer and place lids on jars.
7. Put each jar in a milk carton and close door.
8. Wait 15 minutes.
9. Remove jars and record temperatures one by one being careful not to mix the jars up.
10. Replace lids and return jars to same milk cartons and close the doors.
11. Wait 15 minutes.
12. Remove jars and lids. Record temperatures.
13. Discussion.
14. Do computation on worksheet. Discussion.

X. Discussion

1. What is happening to the temperature of the water in each jar?
2. Which jar is losing the most heat?
3. Which jar retained the most heat?

XI. Extensions

1. How do we insulate our bodies?
2. Why do people in Alaska and the Arctic wear fur against their body? Why would they wear fur on the outside?
3. How do we insulate our homes?
4. How do we insulate pipes?
5. Why does an animal's fur get thicker in the winter?
6. How are animals insulated?

XII. Curriculum Coordinates

Language Arts

1. Sequencing and writing sentences about results.

Art

1. Design a poster asking people to insulate to save energy.

NAME _____

CARTONS 'N COTTON

	BEGINNING TEMP.	15 MINUTE TEMP.	30 MINUTE TEMP.

28

CANNED HEAT

I. Topic Area
Heat Conservation

II. Introductory Statement
Student will understand the effect of color on heat retention.

III. Math Skills
a. Averaging
b. Estimating
c. Measuring

Science Processes
a. Gathering and recording data
b. Interpreting data
c. Applying and generalizing
d. Controlling variables
e. Predicting and hypothesizing

IV. Materials
stop watch
hot plate
celsius thermometer (4 per group)
1 set of 4 soup cans per group (red, green, black, white)

V. Key Question
How does color affect temperature?

VI. Management
1. Activity takes 45-60 minutes.
2. Done outside in small groups.
3. Use a stopwatch to keep time.
4. Teacher or responsible student can keep the time.

VII. Procedure
1. Need to gather cans ahead of time—they should all be the same kind.
2. Cans need to be painted 4 separate colors per group—(red, green, black, white). If not available, cans may be covered with paper.
3. Need to boil water and measure equal amounts into each can (starting temperature should be 90 C.—it may be necessary to have some cold water available to stabilize temperature).

VIII. What the Students Will Do
1. Predict what color can will retain the most heat.
2. Record prediction on class chart.
3. Measure and record temperatures.
4. Wait 5 minutes.
5. Measure and record temperature.
6. Continue process until 30 minutes have passed.
7. Make a bar graph of the results.

IX. Discussion
1. What color jacket would keep you warmest? dark colors
2. Where would it be best to have black roofs? in the east
3. Why do dark colors retain heat? On the light colors the sun is reflected. On the dark colors the light rays are absorbed.

X. Extensions
1. Different containers could be used (styrofoam, aluminum, paper, etc.)
2. Vary your intervals. Use a 3 minute time span instead of five.

XI. Curriculum Coordinates
Geography
1. Types of houses, types of roofs, colors of structures, animals colors, clothing.

Language Arts
1. If I were an Eskimo...

Social Studies
1. Studies of different climates (tropical, tundra, jungle, etc.)

NAME

CANNED HEAT

WHAT COLOR HOLDS HEAT LONGEST?

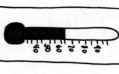

COLORS	STARTING TEMP	5 MIN.	10 MIN.	15 MIN.	20 MIN.	25 MIN.	30 MIN.
RED							
WHITE							
BLACK							
GREEN							

1. RECORD THE STARTING TEMPERATURE IN EACH CAN? SHOULD BE 90°C.
2. WAIT 5 MINUTES - RECORD TEMPERATURE AGAIN.
3. CONTINUE PROCESS FOR 30 MINUTES.

POPPING WITH POWER

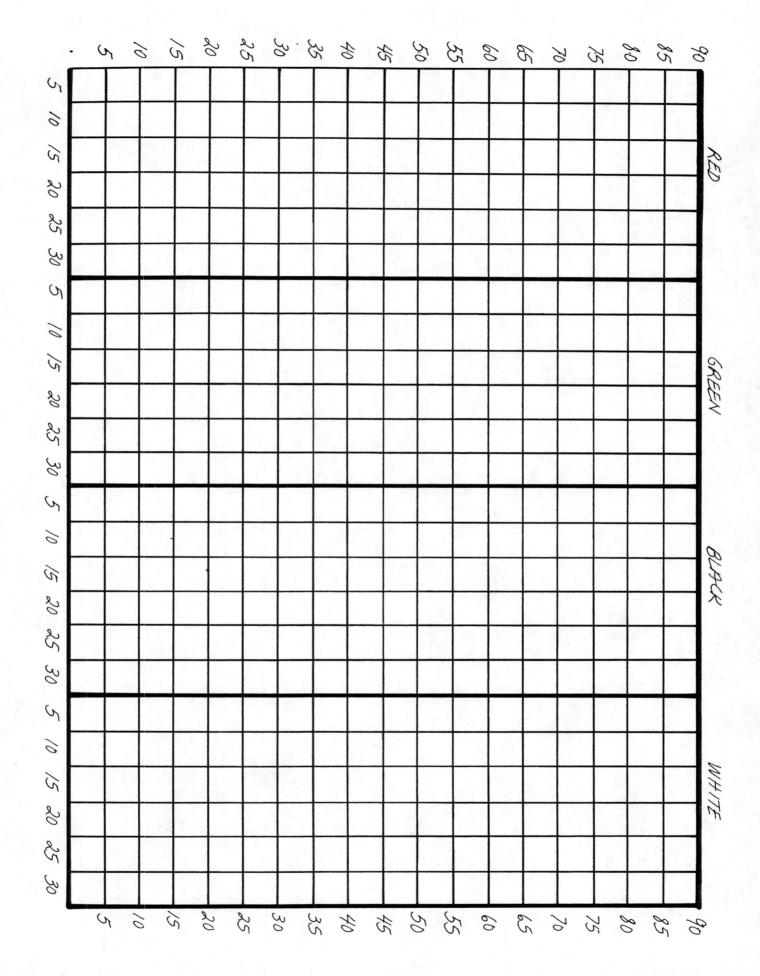

HOT HEAD?

I. Topic Area

Insulating the human head from the heat of the sun.

II. Introductory Statement

Students will learn which kinds of hats give them the best protection from the sun.

III. Math Skills

a. Subtracting
b. Graphing

Science Processes

a. Observing and classifying
b. Predicting and hypothesizing
c. Gathering and recording data
d. Interpreting data

IV. Materials

A varied assortment of summer hats (caps allowed, but hats preferred)
Student work sheets and class sheets for recording
A large class sheet to put on the wall
Pencils and crayons or colored pencils
Small Celsius thermometers

V. Key Question

Which hat or hats give the most protection from the sun's heat and why?

VI. Background Information

If the students haven't used a Celsius thermometer before, it would be helpful to show them how in Math class before doing this investigation.

The material the hat is made of, the color of the hat, the size and shape of it are important factors to discuss in evaluating the results of this investigation.

A child's own body heat can make a difference in the temperature reading. Everyone participating should be as cool and calm as possible.

VII. Management

1. This investigation will take at least 60 minutes. If more time is needed, the coordinating activities could be done in another class period.
2. This activity is done in and from the classroom. Groups of not more than 10 will go outside in turns to test their hats in the sun.
3. The thermometers will be placed on top of the heads and under the hats and they will be at room temperature so that should be recorded on the students work sheets.
4. Then when the students have spent 10 minutes in the sun, the new reading on their thermometer should be recorded on the work sheets and the first reading should be subtracted from the last reading to get the difference. It may vary from 0° to 20°.

VIII. Procedure

1. Ask the children to bring hats to school for a special "Hat Day."
2. Before that day arrives prepare a large class chart from manila graph paper.
3. List the children's names on it.
4. On "Hat Day" have the children model the hats so all may see.
5. Write the Key Question from section V. on the chalkboard and briefly discuss it.
6. Have the children make their predictions as to which hat will be the coolest to wear and mark the predictions on the large chart with a green felt pen.
7. Have them predict the warmest hat and mark it on the chart with a red pen.
8. Hand out the student work sheets and discuss them.
9. Next divide the children into groups of six to ten. The number of thermometers will dictate this.
10. Hand out the Celsius thermometers and have the students record the temperature on their students work sheets.
11. Put the thermometers on their heads and their hats over them.
12. Go outside to line up in the sunlight for 10 minutes.
13. After 10 minutes are up, hats come off and the thermometers should be read right away and the results recorded on the student work sheets.
14. Students should do the subtraction and record the difference on their sheets.
15. Have a class discussion after all have participated. See section X. Discussion.

IX. What the Students Will Do

1. Bring their own hats and model them.
2. Predict which hat will be the coolest to wear and which one will be the warmest.
3. Mark their predictions on the wall graph.
4. Record the room temperature from their Celsius thermometers onto the work sheets.
5. Put the thermometers on their heads and the hats over them.
6. Quietly stand in the bright sunlight for 10 minutes.
7. Quickly remove their hats and the thermometers when the 10 minutes are up.
8. Read the thermometers right away and record the temperatures on their work sheets.
9. Subtract their first temperature reading from the last one to find the difference.
10. Do the bar graph attached to the work sheet.
11. Take part in the class discussion.

X. **Discussion**

1. Which hat had the lowest temperature reading? The one with the smallest difference.
2. Which one had the highest reading? The largest difference? What type of hat? Whose?
3. Which type of hats make best protectors from the sun?
4. How could you maybe change your hat to make it better?

XI. **Extensions**

1. The students could change the colors of their hats by spray painting them. Then the investigation would mainly be based on which colors absorb the sun's rays and which ones reflect them.
2. Other modifications could be made on the hats by the students.
3. The children could make and design their own hats out of a variety of materials.
4. The students could do an experiment on the insulating differences of different colors and textures of human hair.

XII. **Coordinating Subjects**

Language

1. The students can write answers to a given set of questions about the investigation.
2. The students can write a few sentences of their own about the investigation.
3. The students can write their own paragraphs about it.
4. The students can write a creative story or poem about hats.
5. The students can do research reports about hats.

Art

1. The children can make hats out of paper and other materials. They could model them and vote on which one is the coolest, the most unique, the most useful, the most ridiculous, and the most well made.

Health

1. A lesson on human body temperature could involve the use of both Celsius and Fahrenheit thermometers.
2. A lesson on sunburns and sunstroke would be very timely during the hot season of the year.

NAME _____

WHY BE A HOT HEAD?

HATS INSULATE YOUR BRAIN.

1. RECORD YOUR DATA BELOW.

2. SUBTRACT TO FIND THE DIFFERENCE.

TEMPERATURE AFTER THE 10 MINUTES	
TEMPERATURE BEFORE THE 10 MINUTES	
TEMPERATURE DIFFERENCE	

 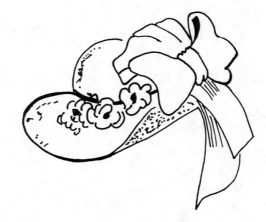 

POPPING WITH POWER

NAME _____

STUDENT NAMES

DEGREES CELSIUS

0 1 2 3 4 5 6 7 8 9 10 11 12 13 14 15 16 17 18 19 20 21 22 23 24 25

DANCING SERPENTINA

I. Topic Area
Changing heat energy into kinetic energy

II. Introductory Statement
Students will learn that heat energy can be changed into kinetic energy.

III. Math Skills
a. Geometry
b. Counting
c. Timing
d. Estimating

Science Processes
a. Predicting and hypothesizing
b. Observing and classifying
c. Gathering and recording

IV. Materials
Coiled snake dittoed on construction paper
Crayons or colored markers
Scissors
Student worksheet
Class graph sheet
Stopwatch or a timepiece with a second hand
Needles
Thimbles

Large thread spools
Some extra long pencils with erasers
Heat energy sources such as: a hot plate with different heat settings, electric fry pan, coffee warmer, a warm radiator, or a warm television

V. Key Question
Why does putting the mounted snake over the heat make it dance?

VI. Background Information
The snake moves when you put it over warm air because the air is rising and pushing up under the snake. The warm air molecules are lively and give off energy.

VII. Management
This investigation can be done in a 45 to 60 minute session. Every child does not need a separate mount for their snake. One mount for each heat source will do. The students may take turns testing their snakes.

VIII. Procedure
1. Set up the heat stations.
2. Hand out dittoed prints of the spiral snake.
3. Direct the class to color and cut out their snakes.
4. Next hand out the student worksheet and explain it.
5. Demonstrate how to make a stand to mount the snake on by putting the pencil in the hole in the spool, sticking the needle into the pencil's eraser, and placing the thimble atop the needle.
6. Then show the class how to mount the hole in the center of the paper snake on top of the thimble.
7. Tell them they will be putting their mounted snakes over the heat source and that they must exercise a great deal of caution not to touch the heated surface.
8. Put the key question on the board and read it aloud together.
9. Explain to them that they are going to count and record the number of times their snake circles around the mount in 60 seconds. Also explain that they must make an estimate first and record it and then observe the snake while it is being timed and record that so they can see how good they are at predicting.
10. Have them take turns doing the testing.
11. Graph each child's results on the class graph sheet.
12. Have a class discussion about the results.

IX. What the Students Will Do
1. Color and cut out the snakes.
2. Make the stand and mount the snake on it.
3. Place the snake on the heat source and predict how many times it will go around.
4. Record the prediction and time and count the snakes revolutions.
5. Record the actual number of times per minute and find the difference between the prediction and the actual count.
6. Record the difference.
7. Participate in the class discussion.

X. Extensions
1. Study a unit about snakes.
2. Find out about the snakes in the students' environment.

XI. Coordinating Subjects
1. Read stories and poems about snakes.
2. Write a story or a poem about a snake.

36

NAME _____

DANCING SERPENTINA

ESTIMATE HOW MANY TURNS SHE
WILL MAKE IN 60 SECONDS.

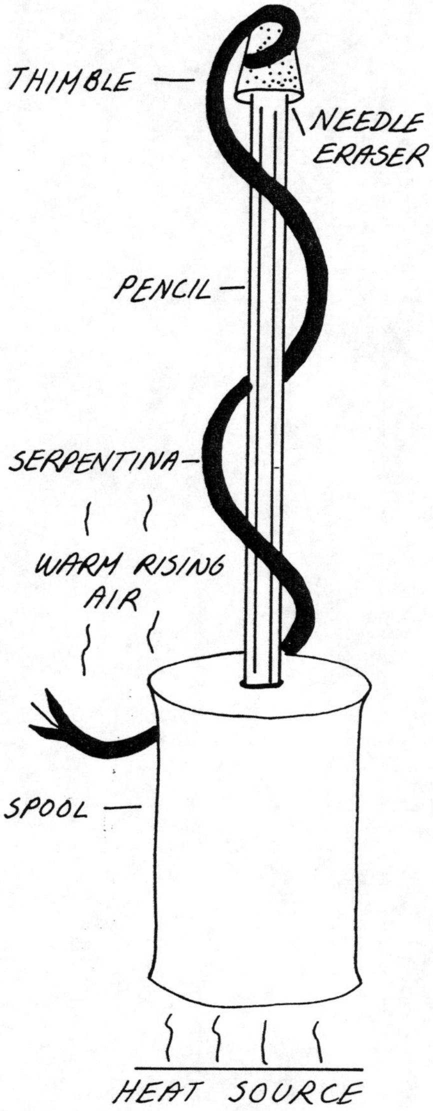

THIMBLE —

NEEDLE
ERASER

ESTIMATE _____

ACTUAL _____

PENCIL —

TO FIND THE DIFFERENCE, SUBTRACT
THE SMALLER NUMBER FROM THE
LARGER NUMBER.

SERPENTINA —

WARM RISING
AIR

SPOOL —

HEAT SOURCE

WHAT GENERATED THE MOTION?

WHAT ARE MOLECULES?

37

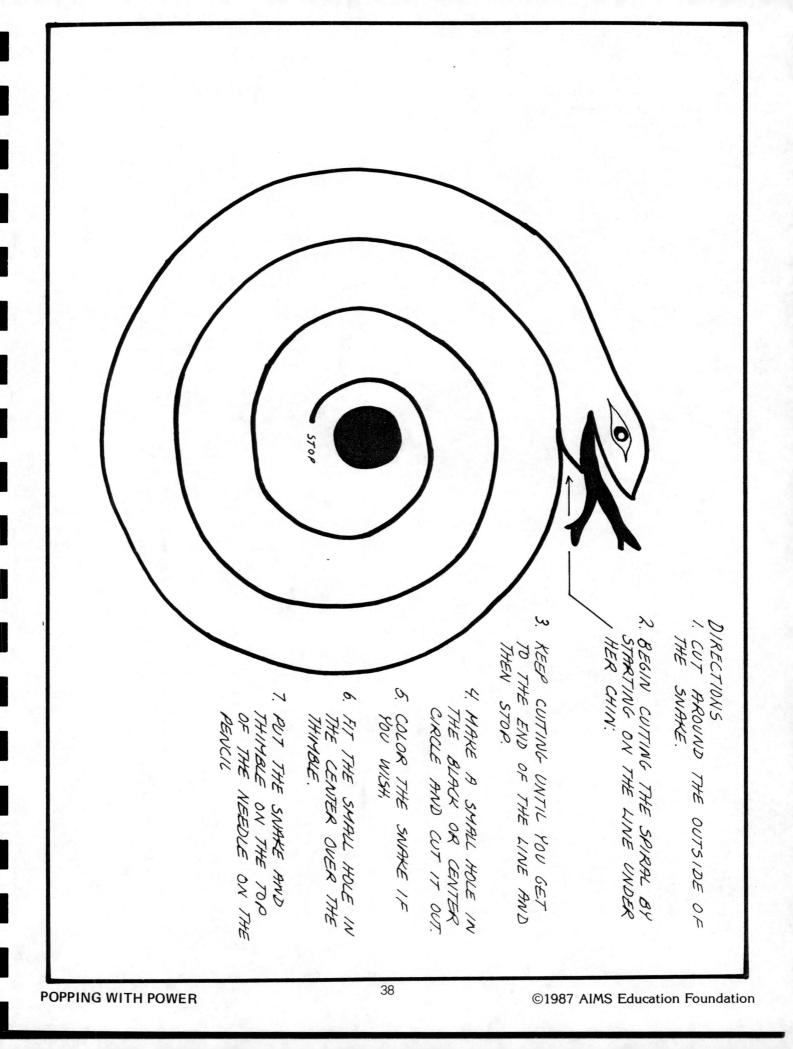

DIRECTIONS
1. CUT AROUND THE OUTSIDE OF THE SNAKE.

2. BEGIN CUTTING THE SPIRAL BY STARTING ON THE LINE UNDER HER CHIN:

3. KEEP CUTTING UNTIL YOU GET TO THE END OF THE LINE AND THEN STOP.

4. MAKE A SMALL HOLE IN THE BLACK OR CENTER CIRCLE AND CUT IT OUT.

5. COLOR THE SNAKE IF YOU WISH.

6. FIT THE SMALL HOLE IN THE CENTER OVER THE THIMBLE.

7. PUT THE SNAKE AND THIMBLE ON THE TOP OF THE NEEDLE ON THE PENCIL.

STOP

POPPING WITH POWER

Puff-Mobiles

I. Topic Area
Physical Science: Energy (wind energy and the wheel)

II. Introductory Statement
Students will make a straw sail car (Puff-Mobile) that uses the wheel as a simple machine and a sheet of paper to "catch the energy" of the wind.

III. Math Skills
Measurement:
  metric
Graphing
Estimating

Science Processes
Gathering and
  recording data
Analyzing and
  generalizing

IV. Materials
Plastic straws (10 per group)
Wooden beads with holes large enough for straws to go through easily
Straight pins
1 sheet of paper 8½ " × 11 " per group

V. Key Question
How far can you blow your Puff-Mobile in 5 seconds?

VI. Management
This activity will take 1-1½ hours.

VII. Procedure
1. Divide the class into groups of 2-3 children.
2. Allow approximately half the time for construction of Puff-Mobiles.
3. Assign jobs in the groups: Puffer, Recorder, Timer.
4. Make sure that each group uses *all* alloted straws and beads.
5. The paper may be cut, if desired.
6. The class and teacher need to determine the number range to be used on the graph after all measurements have been taken.

VIII. What the Students Will Do
1. Students will construct Puff-Mobiles.
2. Students will decide in their groups who will do the final puffing.
3. Students will predict the distance their Puff-Mobile will travel.
4. Students will measure the distance their Puff-Mobile travels in 5 seconds.
5. Students will record and graph results.

IX. Discussion
1. How important is the wheel? (very important to the development of modern civilization, as it has made transportation easier) How are wooden beads like a wheel? (round)
2. Could your Puff-Mobile have moved without wheels? (probably not) What might happen if the wheels were flat? (harder to move—greater friction)
3. Did a sail help? (Yes. It provided the surface against which the source of energy, human puffing, propelled the mobile.)
4. What other ways could we "puff" our mobiles? (a hair blower, a fan)
5. What other kinds of vehicles use the wind to move?
6. What makes a real car move? (a gasoline engine)

X. Extensions
1. Roll the Puff-Mobiles down an incline plane. Record and graph results. How were the results different?

XI. Curriculum Coordinates
Language Arts
1. Write a story, poem, or play (humorous or serious) about the invention of the wheel.
2. Make a comic strip of the history of the wheel.
3. Write a poem or story about the "power of puffing"

Social Studies
1. Research the history of the wheel.
2. Research the history of the other 5 basic machines: level, pulley, wedge, gear wheels, incline plane.
3. Make a time line of inventors and/or inventions.
4. List as many uses for a wheel as can be found (for example, baby carriage, water wheel, pizza cutter, bicycles, grinding wheel, etc.).
5. Research sail planes and other wind-powered vehicles.
6. Make a list of everything you see in one week that has wheels.
7. Collect pictures of how we use wind as a source of energy.

Art
1. Make a picture using only circles.
2. Invent a fantastic machine that moves on wheels.
3. Make a collection of wheels.
4. Make a collection of round things that are usable and movable.
5. Design a way to move something very heavy (sperm whale?) without using wheels. Do the same thing using wheels.

Music
1. Learn the song, "Puff, The Magic Dragon."

_____ _____

_____ _____

Names

Puff like a dragon...
How far can you blow your Puff-Mobile in 5 seconds?

What to do! 1. Build a Puff-Mobile using 10 straws, 4 beads, straight pins, and 1 sheet of paper.

2. You may cut the straws and paper, but you must use __all__ the materials.

	My Guess	Measured Distance
Puff-Mobile 1	_____	_____
Puff-Mobile 2	_____	_____
Puff-Mobile 3	_____	_____
Puff-Mobile 4	_____	_____
Puff-Mobile 5	_____	_____
Puff-Mobile 6	_____	_____
Puff-Mobile 7	_____	_____
Puff-Mobile 8	_____	_____
Puff-Mobile 9	_____	_____
Puff-Mobile 10	_____	_____

PUFF

MOBILES

Names _____

Car Number

10 9 8 7 6 5 4 3 2 1

Distance Traveled

Wind Rollers

I. Topic Area
Estimating and measuring the kinetic energy of the wind in moving an object.

II. Introductory Statement
The children will learn that the triangular points on the circle will act as sails that catch the wind and cause the circle to move.

III. Math Skills
Estimating
Measuring
Geometry

Science Processes
Predicting and hypothesizing
Observing and classifying
Gathering and recording data

IV. Materials
Tagboard
Pencil
Scissors
Compass (optional)

Metric tapes or metric sticks
Metric wheel (optional)
Student worksheets

V. Key Question
How does the wind make the circle move along?

VI. Background Information
Wind has kinetic energy which is the energy of moving things. It comes from a Greek word for "move." The wind can push, pull or lift things. The tagboard circle has potential energy or stored energy. When the wind pushes against the triangular sails or blades on the circle, the circle moves rapidly. The circle's potential energy has been changed into kinetic energy.

VII. Management
This investigation must be done on a breezy, windy day. It can be done with the entire class or with small groups. It may take at least 60 minutes unless only a few do it. Use a cement surface or blacktop to start. It will roll on the grass, too.

VIII. Procedure
1. Tell the children they will each be making a fun toy that will help them learn about the power and energy of the wind. Write *potential* and *kinetic* on the board. Briefly discuss them.
2. Each child must have scissors, pencil, and a student worksheet.
3. Give each student a *dittoed tagboard* diagram of the circle *or* a small paper plate.
4. Cut around the outside of the circle first. Then poke a little hole in the center and cut the little lines just up to but not through the inner circle. If using a paper plate, use the diagram as a guide for cutting the plate (6" paper plates work well).
5. Bend one point or sector up and the other one down, and so on around the circle.
6. Explain that they will be going outside to try out their wind roller to see how fast and how far it will go.
7. Go over the worksheet with them and have them write down their estimates.
8. Assign partners to help with measuring.
9. As you go outside be sure measuring tapes and sticks are taken along. Also take worksheets and pencils.
10. Get lined up outside and take turns.
11. After measuring be sure each distance is recorded.
12. Back in the room do the rest of the worksheet.
13. Have a class discussion. See suggestions under X.

IX. What the Students Will Do
1. Cut out the tagboard circle according to the teacher's instructions.
2. Write down an estimate as to how far their Wind Roller will go.
3. Take it out and test it. Do three trials.
4. Measure and record.
5. Evaluate the best trial.
6. Compare results to other students'.
7. Discuss variables that affect distance (type of surface, amount of wind, rolling technique, weight of paper).

X. Discussion
1. How did the wind make the circle roll?
2. What kind of energy does the wind have?
3. Before the circle began to roll, what kind of energy did it have?
4. When it was rolling what kind of energy did it have?
5. What other kinds of energy are there?
6. What else can the wind do besides push things?
7. How could we improve our Wind Rollers?
8. Form a team to make and test a better Wind Roller. Have a contest.

X. Extensions
1. Study about windmills.
2. Study about sailboats and ships.
3. Do some things with model gliders.
4. Study about wind and weather.

XII. Coordinating Subjects
Language Arts
1. Write a story about some adventures you had while chasing your Wind Roller around the world.
2. Read some poems about the wind.

Wind Roller Directions:

This pattern may be duplicated on tag board or used as a pattern with 6" paper plates.

1. *Cut around the outside of the circle.*

2. *Punch a small hole in the center and cut each short line (radius) from the center to the edge of the inner circle.*

3. *Fold the points (sectors). Fold one up and one down alternately, until all are folded.*

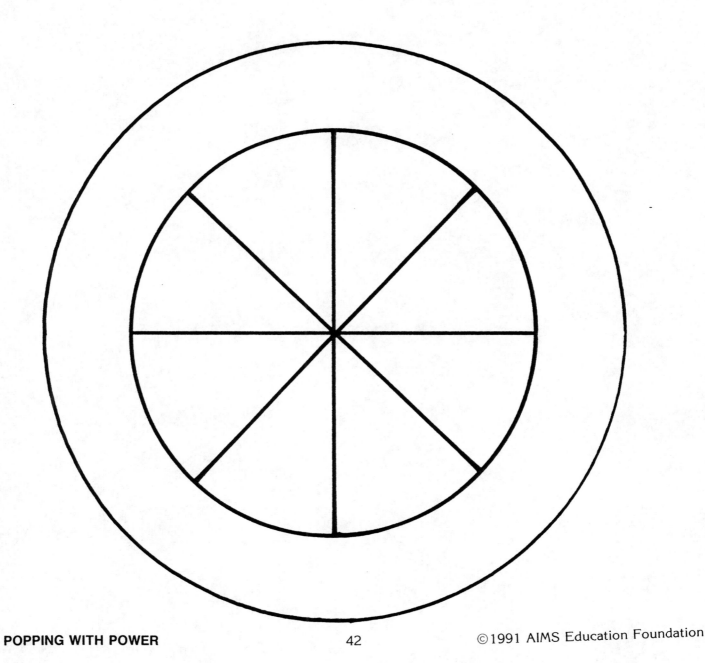

WIND Rollers

* **Predict**
My wind roller loves a windy day.
My estimate _____ (how far I think it will go).

* **Gather and Record**
Measured distance for three trials:
    1st trial _____
    2nd trial _____
    3rd trial _____

* **Put a star next to your best trial !**

* **Evaluate**
My best distance is _____. I think this is because
_____
_____.

* **Compare**
Collect "best distance" data from three other classmates and record.

_____
(name-distance)

_____
(name-distance)

_____
(name-distance)

WIND Rollers

* *Analyze*

Describe how these distances are the same or different from yours.

_____

_____

_____

* *Evaluate and Apply*

What changes would you make if you were entering a "wind roller" in a "longest roll" contest?

_____

_____

_____

BLOW YE WINDS

I. Topic Area
Physical Science—Wind force and suspension bridges

II. Introductory Statement
Students will learn about the effect of wind forces on suspension bridges and their stability.

III. Math Skills
a. Measuring
b. Estimating
c. Geometry

Science Processes
a. Observing and classifying
b. Controlling variables
c. Gathering and recording data
d. Applying and generalizing
e. Predicting and hypothesizing

IV. Materials
ditto paper 8½″ by 11″ (15 to 20 sheets)
cellophane tape
thread or thin string
protractor
scissors
2 meter sticks
stick mounted on board
2 equal size chairs with tall backs
2 hair blowers or fans with 2 speeds

V. Key Question
How does the force of wind effect a suspension bridge?

VI. Background Information
Suspension bridges are supported by tall towers and suspended cables attached to a decking. These bridges are very graceful and must support much weight. Engineers must be knowledgeable of weather conditions, types of metals used, wind forces as well as other factors when they design and construct such a bridge.

The greatest enemy of a suspension bridge is wind. As this investigation shows, it is not necessarily how strong a wind may be, but the combination of the wind force and the direction it takes. At times a strong, steady wind can do less damage than lighter gusts coming from several directions at once.

Modern suspension bridge design and construction must consider safety in all sorts of weather. The decking is designed to give stability to the entire suspension bridge structure. Box girders and trusses are used as stiffening supports for stability. Triangular shapes and girders are frequently used since the triangle is the strongest shape and cannot be twisted easily.

Modern decking and girders are often prefabri-cated, made in factories, and then hoisted into place above a river or bay. This method saves builders materials, money, and time. Modern decking is shaped more like the body of an aircraft, permitting wind to move freely around the deck and thus adding stability to the entire bridge structure.

VII. Management
1. Suspension bridge of paper should be folded, cut, and constructed by the teacher or an adult, prior to the student investigation. Allow 30 minutes to do this.
2. Suspension bridge without triangular decking should be suspended carefully between 2 like size chairs. Bridge should be suspended between the chairs by tying string or thread cables which have been inserted between folded down taped, sides of the bridge.
3. This investigation is best done as a total class activity. Allow 30 minutes for the testing of the bridge without, and with the triangular decking at various wind speeds and from different angles.
4. Hair dryers or fans with 2 varying speeds will be used as the wind source. Fasten 1 metric ruler horizontally to the supported stick and place under the bridge center.
5. Several observers and recorders will be needed to watch and record the amount of sway at each speed and angle.

VIII. Procedure
1. Teacher will construct suspension bridge according to the attached directions prior to class investigation.
2. Teacher and student helpers will carefully suspend bridge between 2 identical sized chair backs. The string "cables" will be tied to the chairs.
3. Teacher will guide discussion about the bridge construction, pointing out the v-shape and the fact that there is no decking.
4. Students and teacher will use the blower or fan at various speeds and angles to test the bridge stability. Results will be recorded on the chart.
5. Students will estimate the amount of movement or sway in cm with the wind source at various speeds when the triangular decking is added to make bridge 2.
6. After the triangular decking pieces have been added to the bridge, students and teacher will use the blower or fan, the 2 wind speeds and various angles to test this bridge stability. Results will be recorded on the chart.
7. Teacher will guide discussion, helping students determine the geometric shapes used in construction to stabilize the bridge and the various effects of the wind force.

IX. What the Students Will Do

1. Students will examine the teacher made suspension bridge and participate in discussion about the first bridge design.
2. The first bridge, without decking support, will be tested for wind effect at the two speeds and angle changes. Two blowers can be used to produce the cross-wing simulation. Results will be recorded on worksheet chart.
3. Students will predict what will happen to the bridge at various wind speeds and from various directions when the triangular decking supports are added. Estimates of sway in cm will be recorded.
4. Triangular decking pieces are added and students will test this bridge using the same blower speeds and angle directions. Results are to be recorded on the chart.
5. Students will compare data, predictions, discuss and make generalizations.

X. Discussion

1. What will happen to bridge 1 when the wind blows at the different speeds and from different directions?
2. Why do you think this happened?
3. What do you think will happen when the triangular decking is added, and why?
4. What were the results when you tested bridge 2?
5. What happens when 2 wind sources are used from opposite directions?
6. Make some generalizations about wind force and its effect on a suspension bridge.

XI. Extensions

1. Collect pictures and read about suspension bridges.
2. Invite a civil engineer or architect in to your classroom to talk about design and construction.
3. Read poems about the wind.
4. Find out more about aerodynamics and wind.
5. Read about wind farms.

X. Curriculum Coordinates

Art
Literature
Research

NAME_____

BLOW YE WINDS

RECORD YOUR DATA

SPEED	ANGLE OF WIND SOURCE	BRIDGE 1 NO DECKING	BRIDGE 2 WITH DECKING	
			ESTIMATES	ACTUAL
HIGH LOW	STRAIGHT ON →	————CM CM	————CM CM	————CM CM
HIGH LOW	LEFT 45° ↘	————CM CM	————CM CM	————CM CM
HIGH LOW	RIGHT 45° ↗	————CM CM	————CM CM	————CM CM
HIGH LOW	ABOVE BRIDGE	————CM CM	————CM CM	————CM CM
HIGH LOW	BELOW BRIDGE	————CM CM	————CM CM	————CM CM
HIGH LOW	2 FANS AT OPPOSITE SIDES ↓↙	————CM CM	————CM CM	————CM CM

WRITE 5 SENTENCES TO TELL WHAT HAPPENED TO THE BRIDGE.
WHICH ANGLE AND SPEED DAMAGED THE BRIDGE MOST?

21 CM

FOLD

FOLD

FOLD

12 CM

CUT 7 OR MORE

POPPING WITH POWER

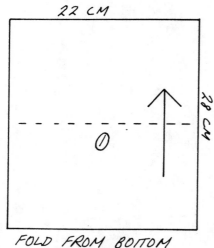

22 CM

28 CM

① FOLD FROM BOTTOM TO TOP.

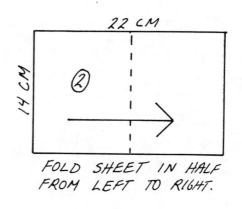

22 CM

14 CM

②

FOLD SHEET IN HALF FROM LEFT TO RIGHT.

BRIDGE CONSTRUCTION DIRECTIONS

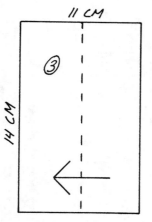

11 CM

14 CM

③

FOLD SHEET IN HALF, FROM RIGHT TO LEFT.

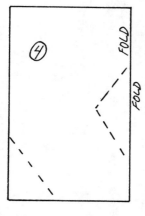

④ FOLD

PLACE PATTERN ④ ON FOLDED PAPER. MAKE SURE V-CUT OF PATTERN IS ALONG FOLD EDGE OF PAPER. CUT OUT.

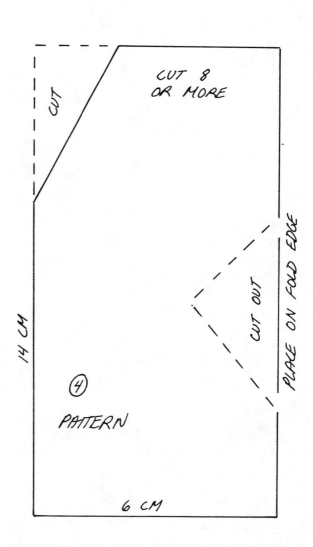

CUT

CUT 8 OR MORE

14 CM

CUT OUT

PLACE ON FOLD EDGE

④

PATTERN

6 CM

48

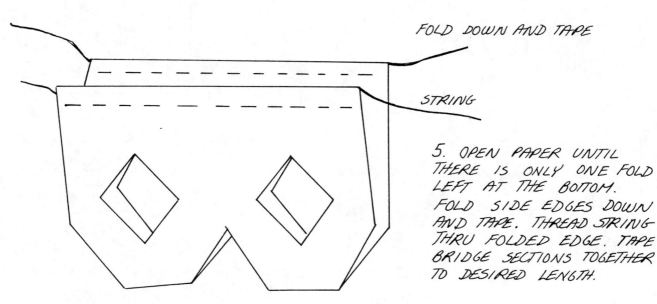

FOLD DOWN AND TAPE

STRING

5. OPEN PAPER UNTIL THERE IS ONLY ONE FOLD LEFT AT THE BOTTOM. FOLD SIDE EDGES DOWN AND TAPE. THREAD STRING THRU FOLDED EDGE. TAPE BRIDGE SECTIONS TOGETHER TO DESIRED LENGTH.

6. FOLD SMALL SHEET OF PAPER INTO FOURTHS AS SHOWN. TAPE INTO TRIANGULAR SHAPES, TAPE EDGES, POSITION ACROSS JOINTS OF BRIDGE TO MAKE BRIDGE 2.

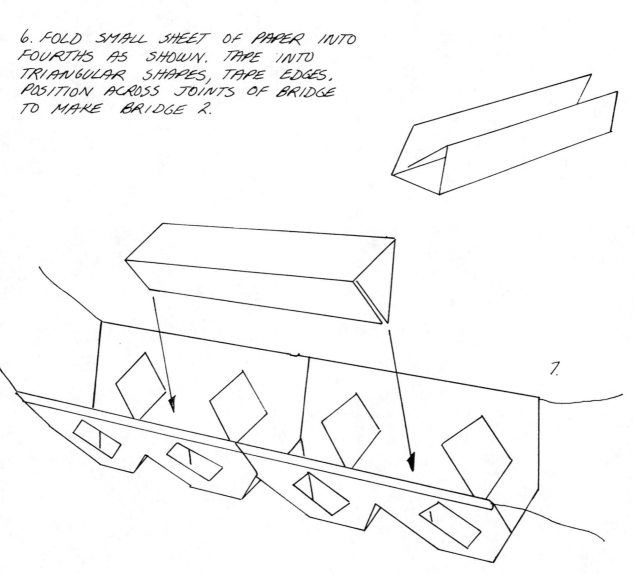

7.

POPPING WITH POWER

©1987 AIMS Education Foundation

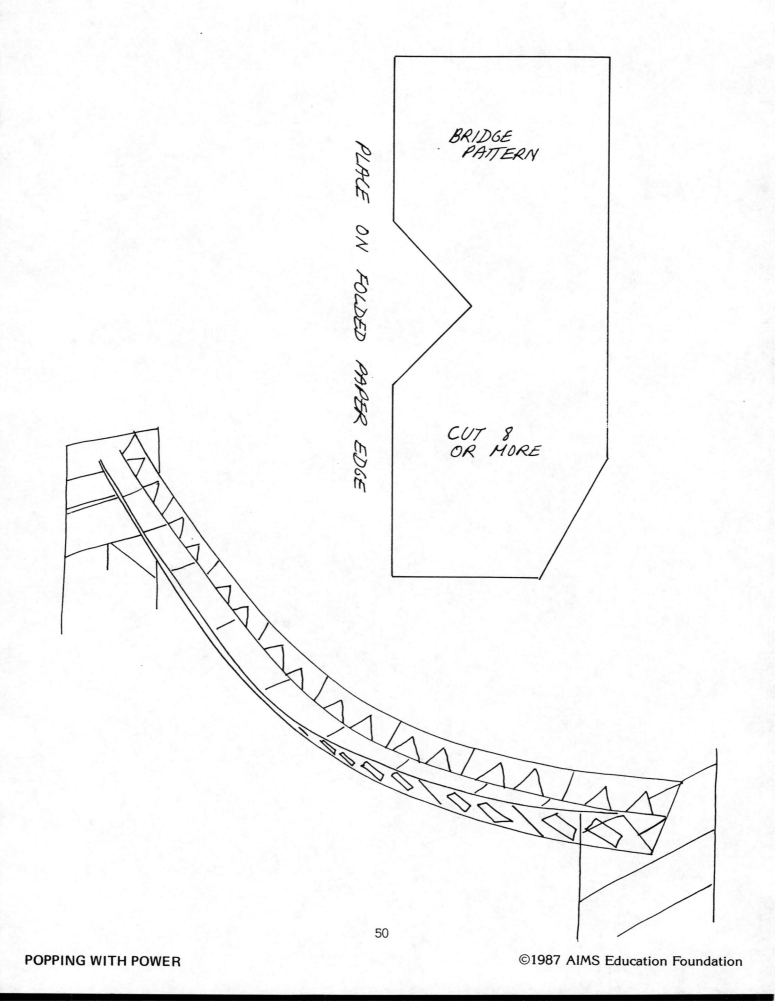

BRIDGE
PATTERN

PLACE ON FOLDED PAPER EDGE

CUT 8
OR MORE

SAVE A WATT

I. Topic Area
Energy—Electric Meter

II. Introductory Statement
Students will learn how to read an electric meter.

III. Math Skills

Math Skills
a. Place value
b. Clockwise/Counter-clockwise
c. Subtraction
d. Multiplication
e. Estimating
f. Graphing

Science Processes
a. Gathering and recording data
b. Observing and classifying
c. Applying and generalizing

IV. Materials
Electric meter at home
Demonstration electric meter dials (teacher made)
Construction paper
Fasteners
Glue

V. Key Question
How much electricity does your family use at home in one day?

VI. Background Information
Many people say they are paying for electric power; however, this is not really correct. Power is the rate at which energy is delivered. You do not pay for the rate energy is delivered but rather the quantity of energy delivered during a specific time period.

A watt-hour is a very small unit of energy. A kilowatt-hour is 1000 watt-hours. Energy is sold by the kilowatt-hours. The kilowatt hour tells us how much electrical energy is being used. The cost of a kwh varies from community to community because of many factors such as: kind of fuel used to run the generators and expense of delivering the electrical energy to the consumers.

A meter records the energy used by all the electrical circuits in your home. The speed of the motor turning the dials varies with the electric energy being used. Older homes have four dials on the meter, and newer homes have five dials. The dials on the electric meter record kilowatt-hours by units of 100,000, 10,000, 1,000, 100, and 10. When the pointer is between two numbers, read the lower number. When the pointer is on 0 or between 0 and 1, read it as 0. When the pointer is between 0 and 9 read it as 9 as 0 stands for 10. We write 0 instead of 10 when the pointer is directly on 0 because we cannot write a two-digit number.

VII. Management
1. Class period one 30-45 minutes—Practice reading demonstration meter, make student meters (optional), estimate.
2. Homework—Record the meter readings in your home, subtract.
3. Class period two 45-60 minutes—Worksheet page 2.

VIII. Procedure
1. Cut out the five circles and glue them on construction paper for the whole class to practice reading meters. You can ditto enough sets for each child to have a practice meter.
2. Make sure that the circle farthest to the right has the numbers in the clockwise direction. Circles alternate after that.
3. Attach fasteners to arrows at center of circles.
4. Read the dials from *right* to *left* and copy the numbers in the same order.
5. Practice reading and recording.

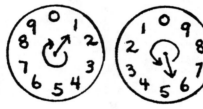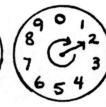

This reading is 1 5 9 8 2.

6. Estimate how many kilowatt-hours your home will use in one day.
7. Send worksheet home to record meter readings. Stress that the readings *must* be done at the same time each day.
8. Subtract the readings and discuss.
9. Graph. The teacher will need to decide on the scale for the graph.
10. Call the electric company to find out the cost of one kilowatt-hour.
11. Multiply to find the cost of one day's electricity. (If you used this figure to find the cost of your electric usage for a month, it would not be totally accurate. Other factors are considered: how far over a minimum number of kilowatt-hours, whether your house is all-electric, disabled person in house, etc.)

IX. What the Students Will Do

1. Practice reading a meter from teacher's demonstration meter.
2. Estimate how many kilowatts their home will use in one day.
3. Take paper home to record meter readings.
4. Subtract the readings.
5. Discussion questions.
6. Graph their results and results from four friends.
7. Multiply to find cost of one day's electric usage.

X. Discussion

1. Think of some reasons why other families used more or less kilowatt-hours. (larger homes, more people, more appliances, more lights, fireplaces, etc.)
2. By what source is your home heated or cooled?
3. Discuss reasons for using more or less kilowatts during different months of the year.

XI. Extensions

1. Record meter reading during a 12-hour period (7 am to 7 pm) and again compare for the following 12-hour period (7 pm to 7 am). Compare usage and discuss results.
2. Record your use for 1 week. What is your daily average? How far off was this from your one day use?
3. See the attached sheet of Home Electrical Appliances and check off the ones that use the most energy in your home.

XII. Curriculum Coordinates

1. Students can collect pictures of appliances which use electricity. These pictures can be classified as: battery vs. plug-in, energy-savers vs. energy-users, convenience vs. luxury.
2. Make a mural of sources of energy: coal, nuclear power, water, wind, solar, and natural gas. Find or draw pictures to fit into each category.

Home Electrical Appliances

Blender	15
Coffee Maker	106
Dishwasher	363
Frying Pan	186
Microwave Oven	190
Range with Oven	1175
Toaster	33
Trash Compactor	50
Refrigerator/Freezer (frostless)	1829
Clothes Dryer	993
Iron	144
Washing Machine	103
Water Heater	4219
Room Air Conditioner	860
Attic Fan	377
Window Fan	170
Hair Dryer	14
Radio	86
TV, color, tube type	660
TV, color, solid state	440
Clock	17
Sewing Machine	11
Vacuum Cleaner	46

**estimated kwh consumed annually

Checklist is from the *Energy-Environment Source Book*, by J. Fowler, published by National Science Teachers Association, 1979.

NAME _____

SAVE A WATT

HOW MUCH ELECTRICITY DOES YOUR FAMILY USE AT HOME IN 1 DAY?

PRACTICE READING A METER, THEN ESTIMATE HOW MANY KILOWATT HOURS YOUR HOME WILL USE IN ONE DAY.

_____
KWH ESTIMATE

DAY 2 _____

DAY 1 _____

SAME TIME EACH DAY!

KWH = KILOWATT HOUR!

RECORD THE METER READINGS IN YOUR HOME FOR 2 DAYS.

SUBTRACT.

HOW MANY KILOWATT HOURS DID YOU USE?

POPPING WITH POWER

NAME_____

HOW DOES YOUR USE COMPARE WITH THAT OF OTHER FAMILIES?

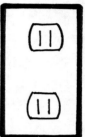

DESIGN A BAR GRAPH AND GRAPH YOUR RESULTS.

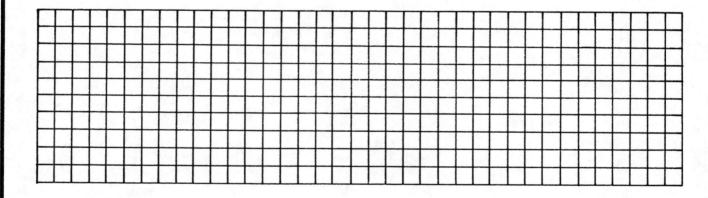

CALL THE ELECTRIC COMPANY TO SEE HOW MUCH ONE KWH COSTS.

HOW MUCH DID ONE DAY'S ELECTRICITY COST?_____

54

NAME _____

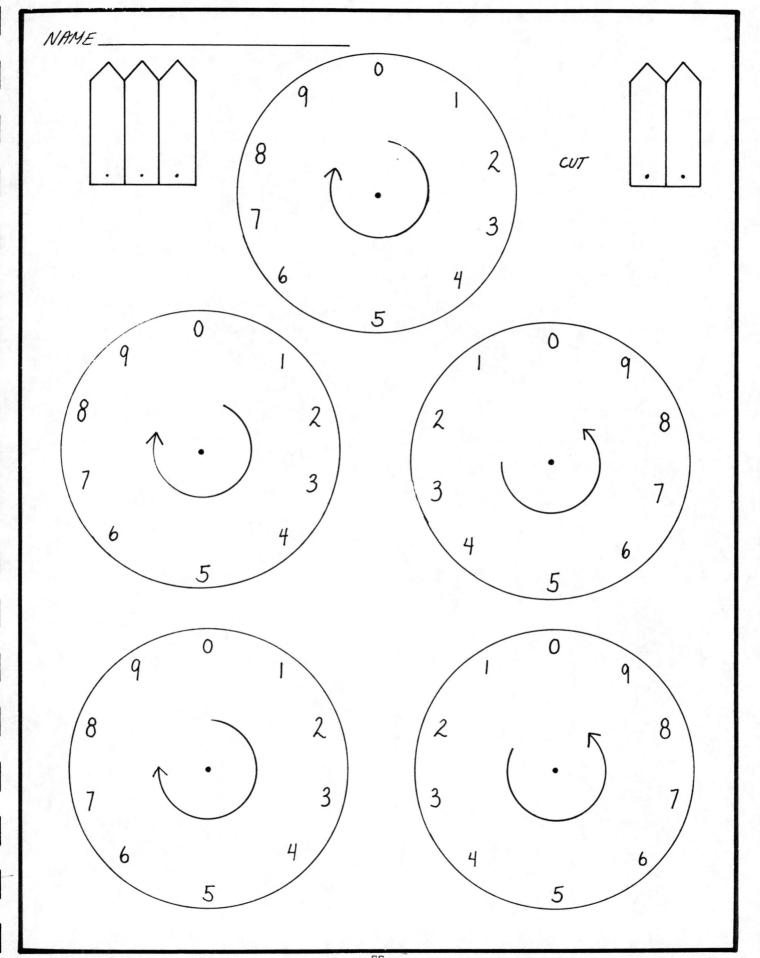

CUT

POPPING WITH POWER

©1987 AIMS Education Foundation

 # STATIC MAGIC

I. Topic Area
Static electricity

II. Introductory Statement
The student will have a variety of experiences with static electricity; discover what happens to materials when he makes and uses static electricity; records his findings on the work sheets.

III. Math Skills
a. Graphs
b. Estimating
c. Measurement

Science Processes
a. Observing and classifying
b. Predicting and hypothesizing
c. Gathering and recording data
d. Interpreting data
e. Applying and generalizing

IV. Materials
Each group will have:
3 shakers of salt
3 shakers of pepper
3 sheets of colored paper
3 pieces of plastic
3 old nylon stockings
3 pieces of cotton material
3 pieces of wool material
3 balloons
Metric ruler
Clay

V. Key Question
Which material carries the strongest electrical charge?

VI. Background
When something has an electric charge, it is said to be electrically charged. Friction can cause some things to become electrically charged. Objects can become electrically charged by adding or taking away electrons. Static electricity is produced by rubbing two different kinds of material together. Static electricity attracts things to it. Static means "not moving." Sometimes static electric charges or static electricity is called friction electricity. You will discover that charges stay on plastic, rubber, and nylon for a long time.

VII. Management
Two days of 45 minute class sessions. Divide the class into small groups of five to six students. On the tables place the materials needed for the two activities. Place the work sheets near each set of materials.

VIII. Procedure
Tell the students that they can have fun with static electricity (pretend that you are a magic person and show how salt and pepper separate). Encourage the student to ask questions about doing the activities. Have the student look at their work sheets. Students will predict what will happen. They need to verify their predictions on the work sheets after doing the activity.

Mix salt and pepper together on a sheet of paper and spread it evenly. Rub a piece of plastic quickly two or three times and hold it above the salt and pepper. Students should observe that the grains of pepper "jump" to the plastic because pepper is lighter in weight than salt. The pepper should stick to the plastic.

After all the students have investigated on their own, discuss the activity and record data on the graph on the work sheet.
1. What happens when you hold the plastic near the salt and pepper?
2. Why do you think the pepper "jumps" to the plastic?

Test your prediction! Mix salt and pepper and spread it evenly on a sheet of paper. Create static electricity by quickly rubbing the material you are testing with your hand. Place metric ruler in clay to stand it up. Hold it 10 cm. above the salt and pepper. If the pepper is attracted to the material, note the height by recording on the graph. If the pepper is not attracted to the material, renew the charge and test at a lower height. Keep testing until you reach the level of attraction.

IX. What the Students Will Do
Included in procedures.

X. Discussion
1. Do you think you can use static electricity to separate pepper from salt?
2. How can you find out?
3. How will you make static electricity?
4. How can you charge a nylon stocking with electricity?
5. How can you charge the wool material with electricity?
6. How can you charge the balloon with electricity?

XI. Extensions

Experiment with static electricity. Have children try this experiment on different kinds of days, such as dry, sunny days; rainy days; cool, cloudy days and keep records of their observations. If the classroom is carpeted, or has a rug on the floor, children can do the experiment at school. If not, suggest that they do it at home. Suggest that the children shuffle across the rug on each kind of day and touch a metal object such as a doorknob.

1. What did you feel?
2. What did you hear?
3. If the room is darkened, what do you see?
4. What makes the spark?

XII. Curriculum Coordinates

Books

1. Bill, Thelma Harrington, *Thunderstorm*, The Viking Press, Inc., New York, 1960.

Films

1. *Electricity All About Us* (11 minutes, color); Coronet Instructional Films. Demonstrates the nature of static and current electricity.

Filmstrip

1. *Experimenting with Static Electricity* (color); Encyclopedia Britannica. Includes experiments children can do with electrically charged objects.

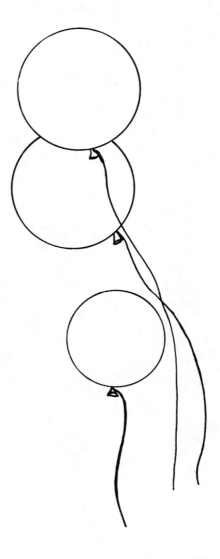

 # STATIC MAGIC

WHICH MATERIAL CARRIES THE STRONGEST ELECTRICAL CHARGE?

TESTING MATERIALS

1. PLASTIC MATERIAL
2. COTTON MATERIAL
3. WOOL MATERIAL
4. NYLON STOCKING
5. BALLOON

PREDICT BY LISTING THE ITEMS FROM STRONGEST TO WEAKEST ATTRACTION.

PREDICTION	ACTUAL
1._____	1._____
2._____	2._____
3._____	3._____
4._____	4._____
5._____	5._____

TEST YOUR PREDICTION!

1. MIX SALT AND PEPPER AND SPREAD IT EVENLY ON A SHEET OF PAPER.

2. CREATE STATIC ELECTRICITY BY QUICKLY RUBBING THE MATERIAL YOU ARE TESTING WITH YOUR HAND.

3. PLACE METRIC RULER IN CLAY TO STAND UP. HOLD THE MATERIAL ABOVE THE SALT AND PEPPER STARTING AT 10 CM. IF THE PEPPER IS ATTRACTED TO THE MATERIAL NOTE THE HEIGHT ON THE GRAPH.

4. IF THE PEPPER IS NOT ATTRACTED TO THE TEST MATERIAL, RENEW THE CHARGE AND TEST AT A LOWER HEIGHT. KEEP TESTING UNTIL YOU REACH THE LEVEL OF ATTRACTION.

GRAPH IT!

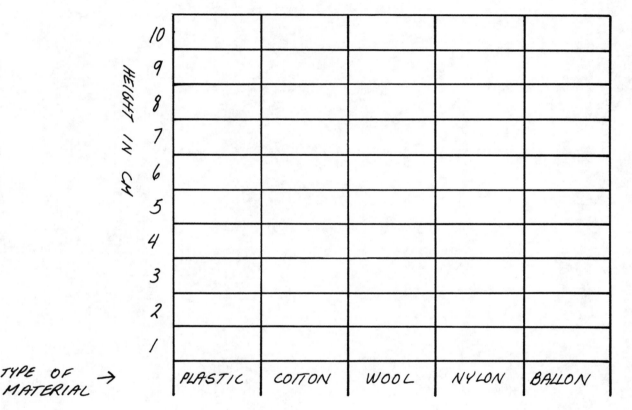

HEIGHT IN CM

	PLASTIC	COTTON	WOOL	NYLON	BALLON
10					
9					
8					
7					
6					
5					
4					
3					
2					
1					

TYPE OF MATERIAL →

SLIP, SLIDING AWAY

I. Topic Area
Physical Energy—Lubricating properties of oil (Mechanics)

II. Introductory Statement
Students will learn about the lubricating properties of various oils.

III. Math Skills
a. Measuring

Science Processes
a. Observing and classifying data
b. Gathering and recording data
c. Applying and generalizing
d. Predicting and hypothesizing

IV. Materials
#10 oil (1 can)
#40 oil (1 can)
edible oil such as corn or vegetable
paper towels
paint brushes
4 pieces of equal size wood, 25 cm × 8 cm × 2 cm (one side needs to be smooth)
4 blocks of equal size wood, 6 cm × 6 cm × 4 cm (edges should be saw-cut and not sanded)
assorted books of these heights when on their sides: 2 cm, 6 cm, 10 cm, 15 cm
stop watch
protractor (optional)

V. Key Question
Which oil lubricates best and reduces friction the most?

VI. Background Information
Friction is the force that opposes the sliding of one object over another. Friction can occur between rough surfaces and even between very smooth surfaces because of molecular attraction. Friction is overcome by the use of fluids to lubricate, or by making the two surfaces of different materials as is found in machinery. Friction is used for brakes on a car, between tires and a road, and between gym shoes and a gym floor.

VII. Management
1. Class period of 30 to 45 minutes.
2. Total class activity under the teacher's guidance.

VIII. Procedure
1. Teacher will paint one side of three of the boards with very thin layers of the different oils.
2. Teacher will rub down each board painted and block painted with paper towels. Be certain not to leave any extra oil on them.

3. Teacher will stress the importance of measuring and starting the block from the same point on each board.
4. Teacher will supervise the raising of the board for each cm. measure to make the different inclined planes.
5. Teacher or an adult aide will operate the stop watch.

IX. What the Students Will Do
1. Students will predict which surface and block will slide easiest and fastest and record on their worksheet.
2. Students will slide the coated blocks down the same coated boards for each of the oil types and different inclined planes and record the results on their worksheet.
3. Students will slide the uncoated block down the uncoated board for each of the different inclined planes and record the results on their worksheet.
4. Teacher or adult will assist students in reading the stopwatch times for each block tested.
5. Students will compare their prediction with the actual timed results.
6. Students will make generalizations.

X. **Discussion**
1. What is your prediction for the fastest sliding block and which board surface?
2. What happened when the uncoated block slid down the uncoated board?
3. Was there any change in time as the inclined plane became steeper?
4. Which painted oil block and surface was the fastest?
5. What happened as the inclined plane slope changed for each of the oil types?
6. What generalizations can you make about oil lubrication and friction?

XI. **Extensions**
1. Use a protractor to measure the various angles made for the inclined plane at the various cm. height changes.
2. Use different liquids to coat other boards and blocks and test them for their lubricating properties.

XII. **Curriculum Coordinates**
Physical Education
1. See how friction is used in sports.
Social Studies
1. Learn how friction is used or overcome in industry.

NAME _____

SLIP, SLIDING AWAY

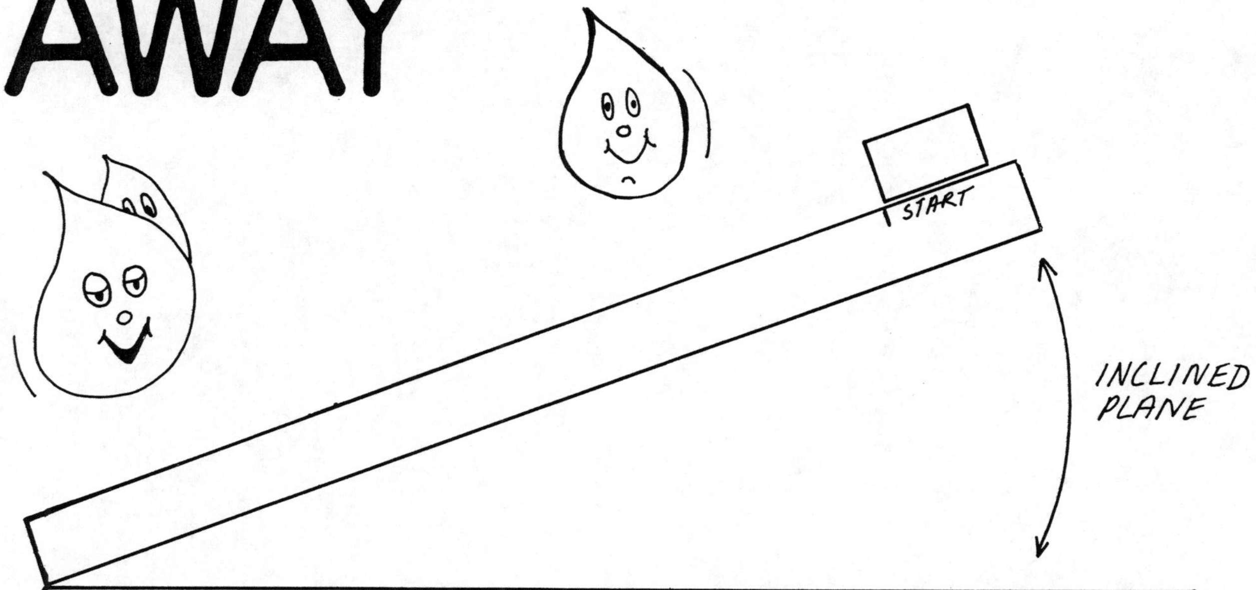

START

INCLINED PLANE

BLOCK	A	B	C	D
TYPE OIL				
2 CM TIME				
6 CM TIME				
10 CM TIME				
15 CM TIME				

RESULTS : _____

_____

_____

_____

POPPING WITH POWER

©1987 AIMS Education Foundation

CATAPULTS

I. Topic Area
Catapults

II. Introductory Statement
Students will observe the distance and height of an object hurled by a student-constructed catapult.

III. Key Question
How could you throw a heavy boulder over a wall?

IV. Math Skills
a. Geometry
b. Measuring length and height

Science Processes
a. Observing and classifying
b. Gathering and recording data

V. Materials
*The following is a list of materials for 1 catapult. Each group of 4 students will be making their own catapult, so purchase materials accordingly.
2 wood blocks
1 strip of metal banding (8" long)
4 nails that won't exceed the width of both blocks
1 small nail
1 rubberband
1 cotton ball
hammer
1 metric tape measure
1 protractor

VI. Background Information
1. A catapult works in a similar fashion to a slingshot or a bow and arrow. In ancient times, warriors used catapults to hurl heavy rocks and pieces of metal across moats and over walls into castles or cities.
2. In this investigation, the metal banding will be referred to as the "arm."

VII. Management
1. Divide class into groups of 4.
2. Give each group 2 wood blocks, 1 strip of metal banding, 1 protractor, 4 long nails, 1 small nail, 1 cotton ball, 1 rubberband, and 1 hammer.
3. Building the catapults will take 20-30 minutes.
4. Directions for building the catapults.
   a. Bend metal banding into an L shape and insert the "L" end in between the two blocks of wood.
   b. Nail the blocks together. Hammer 2 nails on either side of the metal stripping and 2 nails at the other ends of the blocks.
   c. Nail the protractor vertically at the front of the catapult, close to the metal band (arm). If

your protractors don't have holes in them, then tape the protractor onto the wood blocks.
   d. See diagram below.

VIII. Procedure
1. Direct students in building their catapults
2. Instruct each group to select 1 group member to fire the cotton ball, 1 member to spot the height of the cotton ball when in flight, 1 member to spot the landing point, and 1 member (along with the student who is firing) to measure height and length of flight.
3. Firing should be done outside or in a gym, to give all groups enough room.
4. Place catapult on a chair while firing.
5. Place cotton ball at the end of arm and slip rubberband around it to hold it in place.
6. Pull arm back 10 degrees and release. If the cotton ball flies straight up or flies backwards (it might), then fire again.
7. Length is measured at the first spot where the cotton ball hits. The spotter for height should look for the highest point the cotton ball flies.
8. Repeat the firing procedure at 20 degrees through to 90 degrees.

IX. What the Students Will Do
1. Students will build catapults.
2. Student groups will fire the cotton balls and measure the length and height of the flight.
3. Students will record the results of each flight.

X. **Discussion**

1. What angle shot the cotton ball the farthest? What angle shot the cotton ball the highest?

2. Was there a pattern of numbers in your results? (As the arm is pulled down farther, the cotton ball should get more height but less distance.)

3. If you were a medieval warrior, and you were shooting from a distance, what angle would be best? (Students should answer the angle that shot their cotton ball the farthest.)

4. To what angle would you pull the arm if you needed to shoot over a high wall? (Students should recognize the angle that shot the highest.)

5. Compare the catapult theory to throwing a ball, kicking a ball, hitting a ball with a bat, slingshot, and bow and arrow.

XI. **Extensions**

1. Draw a protractor on a portable chalkboard. Take it outside and have the children act as catapults. Hold their arms straight up (90 degrees), then pull back 10 degrees. Have them throw the ball with their arm back only 10 degrees and measure the distance thrown. Repeat at 20 degrees, 30 degrees,...

2. Use a heavier ball on the catapult. Compare results.

3. Use different shapes on the catapult.

XII. **Curriculum Coordinates**

History

1. Teach unit on medieval times.

Research Paper

1. Research the origin of the catapult.

Social Studies

1. Compare ancient methods of weaponry with weapons of modern day.

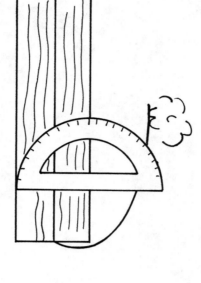

CATAPULTS

ARM PULLED BACK	LENGTH CM	HEIGHT CM
10°		
20°		
30°		
40°		
50°		
60°		
70°		
80°		
90°		

TOTAL _____

AVERAGE 9)‾‾ 9)‾‾

1	26	51	76 30
2	1 27	52	77
3	28	11 53	21 78 31
4	29	54	79
5	2 30	55	80
6	31	12 56	22 81 32
7	32	57	82
8	3 33	13 58	83
9	34	59	23 84 33
10	4 35	60	85
11	36	14 61	24 86 34
12	37	62	87
13	5 38	15 63	88
14	39	64	25 89 35
15	6 40	65	90
16	41	16 66	26 91 YARD 36
17	42	67	92
18	7 43	17 68	93
19	44	69	27 94 37
20	8 45	70	95
21	46	18 71	28 96 38
22	47	72	97
23	9 48	19 73	98
24	49	74	29 99 39
25	50	75	100 METER

10 20

TAPE MEASURE

POPPING WITH POWER

66

The AIMS Program

AIMS is the acronym for "Activities Integrating Mathematics and Science." Such integration enriches learning and makes it meaningful and holistic. AIMS began as a project of Fresno Pacific College to integrate the study of mathematics and science in Grades K-9, but has since expanded to include language arts, social studies, and other disciplines.

AIMS is a continuing program of the non-profit AIMS Education Foundation. It had its inception in a National Science Foundation funded program whose purpose was to explore the effectiveness of integrating mathematics and science. The project directors in cooperation with eighty elementary classroom teachers devoted two years to a thorough field-testing of the results and implications of integration.

The approach met with such positive results that the decision was made to launch a program to create instructional materials incorporating this concept. Despite the fact that thoughtful educators have long recommended an integrative approach, very little appropriate material was available in 1981 when the project began. A series of writing projects have ensued and today the AIMS Education Foundation is committed to continue the creation of new integrated activities on a permanent basis.

The AIMS program is funded through the sale of this developing series of books and proceeds from the Foundation's endowment. All net income from book and poster sales flow into a trust fund administered by the AIMS Education Foundation. Use of these funds is restricted to support of research, development, publication of new materials, and partial scholarships for classroom teachers participating in writing and field testing teams. Writers donate all their rights to the Foundation to support its on-going program. No royalties are paid to the writers.

The rationale for integration lies in the fact that science, mathematics, language arts, social studies, etc., are integrally interwoven in the real world from which it follows that they should be similarly treated in the classroom where we are preparing students to live in that world. Teachers who use the AIMS program give enthusiastic endorsement to the effectiveness of this approach.

Science encompasses the art of questioning, investigating, hypothesizing, discovering and communicating. Mathematics is the language that provides clarity, objectivity, and understanding. The language arts provide us powerful tools of communication. Many of the major contemporary societal issues stem from advancements in science and must be studied in the context of the social sciences. Therefore, it is timely that all of us take seriously a more holistic mode of educating our students. This goal motivates all who are associated with the AIMS Program. We invite you to join us in this effort.

Meaningful integration of knowledge is a major recommendation coming from the nation's professional science and mathematics associations. The American Association for the Advancement of Science in *Science for All Americans* strongly recommends the integration of mathematics, science and technology. The National Council of Teachers of Mathematics places strong emphasis on applications of mathematics such as are found in science investigations. AIMS is fully aligned with these recommendations.

Extensive field testing of AIMS investigations confirms these beneficial results.

1. Mathematics becomes more meaningful, hence more useful, when it is applied to situations that interest students.
2. The extent to which science is studied and understood is increased, with a significant economy of time, when mathematics and science are integrated.
3. There is improved quality of learning and retention, supporting the thesis that learning which is meaningful and relevant is more effective.
4. Motivation and involvement are increased dramatically as students investigate real world situations and participate actively in the process.

We invite you to become part of this classroom teacher movement by using an integrated approach to learning and sharing any suggestions you may have. The AIMS Program welcomes you!

AIMS Education Foundation Programs

A Day With AIMS

Intensive one-day workshops are offered to introduce educators to the philosophy and rationale of AIMS. Participants will discuss the methodology of AIMS and the strategies by which AIMS principles may be incorporated into curriculum. Each participant will take part in a variety of hands-on AIMS investigations to gain an understanding of such aspects as the scientific/mathematical content, classroom management, and connections with other curricular areas. The *A Day With AIMS* workshops may be offered anywhere in the United States. Necessary supplies and take-home materials are usually included in the enrollment fee.

AIMS One-Week Off-Campus Workshops

Throughout the nation, AIMS offers many one-week workshops each year, usually in the summer. Each workshop lasts five days and includes at least 30 hours of AIMS hands-on instruction. Participants are grouped according to the grade level(s) in which they are interested. Instructors are members of the AIMS National Leadership Network. Supplies for the activities and a generous supply of take-home materials are included in the enrollment fee. Sites are selected on the basis of applications submitted by educational organizations. If chosen to host a workshop, the host agency agrees to provide specified facilities and cooperate in the promotion of the workshop. The AIMS Education Foundation supplies workshop materials as well as the travel, housing, and meals for instructors.

AIMS One-Week On-Campus Workshops

Each summer, Fresno Pacific College offers AIMS one-week workshops on the campus of Fresno Pacific College in Fresno, California. AIMS Program Directors and highly qualified members of the AIMS National Leadership Network serve as instructors.

The Science Festival and the Festival of Mathematics

Each summer, Fresno Pacific College offers a Science Festival and a Festival of Mathematics. These two-week festivals have gained national recognition as inspiring and challenging experiences, giving unique opportunities to experience hands-on mathematics and science in topical and grade level groups. Guest faculty includes some of the nation's most highly regarded mathematics and science educators. Supplies and take-home materials are included in the enrollment fee.

The AIMS National Leadership Program

This is an AIMS staff development program seeking to prepare facilitators for a leadership roles in science/math education in their home districts or regions. Upon successful completion of the program, trained facilitators become members of the AIMS National Leadership Network, qualified to conduct AIMS workshops, teach AIMS in-service courses for college credit, and serve as AIMS consultants. Intensive training is provided in mathematics, science, processing skills, workshop management, and other relevant topics.

College Credit and Grants

Those who participate in workshops may often qualify for college credit. If the workshop takes place on the campus of Fresno Pacific College, that institution may grant appropriate credit. If the workshop takes place off-campus, arrangements can sometimes be made for credit to be granted by another college or university. In addition, the applicant's home school district is often willing to grant in-service or professional development credit. Many educators who participate in AIMS workshops are recipients of various types of educational grants, either local or national. Nationally known foundations and funding agencies have long recognized the value of AIMS mathematics and science workshops to educators. The AIMS Education Foundation encourages educators interested in attending or hosting workshops to explore the possibilities suggested above. Although the Foundation strongly supports such interest, it reminds applicants that they have the primary responsibility for fulfilling *current* requirements.

For current information regarding the programs described above, please complete the following:

Information Request

Please send current information on the items checked:

____ *Basic Information Packet* on AIMS materials	____ *AIMS One-Week On-Campus Workshops*
____ *Festival of Mathematics*	____ *AIMS One-Week Off-Campus Workshops*
____ *Science Festival*	____ Hosting information for *A Day With AIMS* workshops
____ *AIMS National Leadership Program*	____ Hosting information for *A Week With AIMS* workshops

Name _____

Address _____
           Street   City   State   Zip

Mail to **AIMS Education Foundation**, P.O. Box 8120, Fresno, CA 93747-8120

AIMS Program Publications

GRADES 5-9 SERIES

Math + Science, A Solution
The Sky's the Limit
From Head to Toe
Fun With Foods
Floaters and Sinkers
Down to Earth
Our Wonderful World
Pieces and Patterns, A Patchwork in Math and Science
Piezas y Diseños, un Mosaic de Matemáticas y Ciencias
Out of This World
Soap Films and Bubbles
Finding Your Bearings
Electrical Connections
Historical Connections in Mathematics

GRADES K-4 SERIES

Fall Into Math and Science
Cáete de Gusto Hacia el Otoño con la Matemáticas y Ciencias
Glide Into Winter With Math and Science
Patine al Invierno con Matemáticas y Ciencias
Spring Into Math and Science
Brinca de Alegria Hacia la Primavera con las Matemáticas y Ciencias
Seasoning Math and Science, Book A (Fall and Winter)
Seasoning Math and Science, Book B (Spring and Summer)
Jawbreakers and Heart Thumpers
Hardhatting in a Geo-World
Popping With Power
Overhead and Underfoot
Primarily Plants
Primariamente Plantas
Primarily Physics
Primariamente Física

GRADES K-6 SERIES

Primarily Bears
Ositos Nada Más
Water Precious Water
Critters
Mostly Magnets

FOR FURTHER INFORMATION WRITE TO:
AIMS Education Foundation • P.O. Box 8120 • Fresno, California 93747-8120

We invite you to subscribe to the
AIMS Newsletter!

Each issue of the AIMS Newsletter contains a variety of material useful to educators at all grade levels. Feature articles of lasting value deal with topics such as mathematical or science concepts, curriculum, assessment, the teaching of processing skills, and historical background. Several of the latest AIMS math/science investigations are always included, along with their reproducible activity sheets. As needs direct and space allows, various issues contain news of current developments, such as workshop schedules, activities of the AIMS National Leadership Network, and announcements of upcoming publications.

The AIMS Newsletter is published monthly, August through May. Subscriptions are on an annual basis only. A subscription entered at any time will begin with the next issue, but will also include the previous issues of that year or volume. Readers have preferred this arrangement because articles and activities within an annual volume are often interrelated.

Please note that an AIMS Newsletter subscription automatically includes duplication rights for one school site for all issues of the Newsletter included in the subscription. Many schools build cost-effective library resources with their subscriptions.

YES! I am interested in receiving the AIMS Newsletter.

Please send the following volumes, subject to availability:

_____	Volume I (1986-87)	$22.50
_____	Volume II (1987-88)	$22.50
_____	Volume III (1988-89)	$22.50
_____	Volume IV (1989-90)	$22.50
_____	Volume V (1990-91)	$22.50
_____	Volume VI (1991-92)	$25.00
_____	Limited offer: Volumes VII & VIII (1992-93 & 1993-94) $45.00	

_____ _____

(Note: Prices may change without notice. For current prices, phone (209) 255-4094 weekdays during office hours-Pacific time.)

Check your method of payment:

☐ Check enclosed in the amount of _____
☐ Purchase order attached (Please be sure it includes the P.O. number, the authorizing signature, and the position of the authorizing person.)
☐ Visa or MasterCard # _____
   (circle one)

Expires_____

Signature_____

Make checks payable to **AIMS Education Foundation**.
Mail to **AIMS Newsletter, P.O. Box 8120, Fresno, CA 93747-8120**.

AIMS Duplication Rights Program

AIMS has received many requests from school districts for the purchase of unlimited duplication rights to *AIMS* materials. In response, the *AIMS Education Foundation* has formulated the program outlined below. There is a built-in flexibility which, we trust, will provide for those who use *AIMS* materials extensively to purchase such rights for either individual activities or entire books.

It is the goal of the *AIMS Education Foundation* to make its materials and programs available at reasonable cost. All income from sale of publications and duplication rights is used to support *AIMS* programs. Hence, strict adherence to regulations governing duplication is essential. Duplication of *AIMS* materials beyond limits set by copyright laws and those specified below is strictly forbidden.

Limited Duplication Rights

Any purchaser of an AIMS book may make up to *200 copies* of any activity in that book for use at *one school site*. Beyond that, rights must be purchased according to the appropriate category.

Unlimited Duplication Rights for Single Activities

An individual or school may purchase the right to make an unlimited number of copies of a single activity. The royalty is $5.00 per activity per school site.

Examples: 3 activities x 1 site   x $5.00 = $15.00
9 activities x 3 sites x $5.00 = $135.00

Unlimited Duplication Rights for Whole Books

A school or district may purchase the right to make an unlimited number of copies of a single, *specified* book. The royalty is $20.00 per book per school site. This is in addition to the cost of the book.

Examples: 5 books   x   1 site   x $20.00 = $100.00
12 books   x   10 sites x $20.00 = $2400.00

Newsletter Duplication Rights

Members of the *AIMS Education Foundation* who receive the *AIMS Newsletter* may make an unlimited number of copies of activities for use only at the member's school site. School districts must join separately for each school desiring to duplicate activities.

Workshop Instructors' Duplication Rights

Workshop instructors may distribute to registered workshop participants: a maximum of 100 copies of any article and /or 100 copies of no more than 8 activities, provided these 6 conditions are met:

1. Since all *AIMS* activities are based upon the *AIMS Model of Mathematics* and the *AIMS Model of Learning*, leaders must include in their presentations an explanation of these two models.
2. Workshop instructors must relate the *AIMS* activities presented to these basic explanations of the *AIMS* philosophy of education.
3. The copyright notice must appear on all materials distributed.
4. Instructors must provide information enabling participants to apply for membership in the *AIMS Education Foundation* or order books from the Foundation.
5. Instructors must inform participants of their limited duplication rights as outlined below.
6. Only student pages may be duplicated.

Written permission must be obtained for duplication beyond the limits listed above. Additional royalty payments may be required.

Workshop Participants' Rights

Those enrolled in workshops in which AIMS student activity sheets are distributed may duplicate a maximum of 35 copies or enough to use the lessons one time with one class, whichever is less. Beyond that, rights must be purchased according to the appropriate category.

Application for Duplication Rights

The purchasing agency or individual must clearly specify the following:

1. Name, address, and telephone number
2. Titles of the books for Unlimited Duplication Rights contracts
3. Titles of activities for Unlimited Duplication Rights contracts
4. Names and addresses of school sites for which duplication rights are being purchased

NOTE: Books to be duplicated must be purchased separately and are not included in the contract for Unlimited Duplication Rights.

The requested duplication rights are automatically authorized when proper payment is received, although a *Certificate of Duplication Rights* will be issued when the application is processed.

Address all correspondence to

Contract Division
AIMS Education Foundation
P.O. Box 8120
Fresno, CA 93747-8120